'Tis education forms the common mind.
Just as the twig is bent, the tree's inclined.
Alexander Pope

This book belongs to

_____

Other books by Jo Kline Cebuhar

SO GROWS THE TREE
Creating an Ethical Will
The legacy of your beliefs and values, life lessons
and hopes for the future
(2010)

USA Book News
National "Best Books 2010" Award
Winner in Health: Aging/50+ category
Finalist in Self Help: General category

Last things first, just in case...
The practical guide to Living Wills and
Durable Powers of Attorney for Health Care
(2006)

Foreward Magazine
2006 Book of the Year Award
Finalist in Family & Relationships category
Finalist in Reference category

USA Book News
National "Best Books 2007" Award
Winner in Health: Medical Reference category
Finalist in Health: Aging/50+ category

Principles of Tax-deferred Exchanging
(1996 and 2001 Revised Edition)

The Workshop Edition
of
SO GROWS THE TREE

Creating an Ethical Will
The legacy of your
beliefs and values, life lessons
and hopes for the future

Jo Kline Cebuhar, J.D.

The Workshop Edition of
SO GROWS THE TREE

Creating an Ethical Will
The legacy of your
beliefs and values, life lessons
hopes for the future
by
Jo Kline Cebuhar, J.D.

Published in the United States of America by
Murphy Publishing
P.O. Box 65370
West Des Moines, Iowa 50265-0370
E-mail: MurphyPublishing@msn.com

ISBN 978-0-9661851-8-8

"If you can dream it, you can do it."
Walt Disney

ᔒ About the Author ᔕ

Jo Kline Cebuhar has been an attorney and entrepreneur for 26 years. As the chairman of Iowa's largest hospice organization, she came to understand the importance of and right to peace and dignity at life's end, which was the path to her first book, **Last things first, just in case... The practical guide to Living Wills and Durable Powers of Attorney for Health Care**.

Whenever Jo spoke, people wanted to know more about Chapter Ten: A legacy of values and beliefs, The Ethical Will. That led to her 2010 book **SO GROWS THE TREE – Creating an Ethical Will**.

Some readers of **SO GROWS THE TREE** preferred to tackle the creation of their Ethical Wills with a little help from their friends and asked for direction on how to use the book in a workshop setting. As the O'Jays put it so well: *"Give the people what they want."* Jo is proud to present here **The Workshop Edition of SO GROWS THE TREE – Creating an Ethical Will**.

Jo is a frequent speaker and workshop leader on Ethical Wills and lives in a state of bliss called Iowa with her husband and two kitties.

ᔒ Acknowledgements ᔕ

You know who you are. Thank you.

ᔒ Join in the Dialogue ᔕ

Please visit *www.SoGrowsTheTree.com* for ideas on how to use *The Workshop Edition of SO GROWS A TREE* as an activity to raise funds or just your consciousness! If you have comments or questions about this book or would like to share an Ethical Will you have created or received or an innovative workshop approach you are using, please contact us at:

www.SoGrowsTheTree.com

To Uncle Bill,
for writing the letter

✍ Table of Contents ✍

**WORKSHOP and SLIDESHOW
SESSION III**

The serial project
A simple outline for an Ethical Will
A prompting outline

Coming together is a beginning.
Keeping together is progress.
Working together is success.
Henry Ford

Rules for this journey
(more like suggestions, really...)

The definition of an Ethical Will is simple: *an Ethical Will is the message of what you stand for.* It's a record of your beliefs and values, life lessons and hopes for the future. It can be expressed as a multimedia slideshow, a family cookbook, an embellished photo album, or a scrapbook journal. You can share a collection of favorite quotations or choose a poem that says it all for you. Or, it can be a simple letter addressed to your loved ones, typed or even handwritten.

The term "workshop" is just as straightforward: it's an opportunity to learn through instruction (in this case, on creating an Ethical Will), practice doing it yourself and then share and discuss the work done by the workshop members ("workshopping"). A workshop is not a competitive sport, and it is not meant to put pressure on you or to compare your skills with others'. The primary goal of *The Workshop Edition of SO GROWS THE TREE* is to provide a way for you, the reader/workshop attendee, to learn about Ethical Wills and then become comfortable with creating your own Ethical Will, knowing that you have a message worth recording and worth sharing.

I have a pretty good idea what you're thinking right about now:

Will I really do this?

Do I have it in me to create an Ethical Will that I am willing to share and that others will really want to hear?

What are the odds that this will turn out to be another one of those well-intentioned "it seemed like a good idea at the time" projects?

As for those doubts, you're not alone. I remember all too well my fears just before I started writing the first edition of *SO GROWS THE TREE* in 2009. Wanting to assist others to get past that hesitancy—the feeling that creating and sharing something memorable from your heart may not be an attainable goal—is what motivated me to write *The Workshop Edition of SO GROWS THE TREE*. Teaching you about Ethical Wills is *my* job. I tell their incredible history, beginning with the Book of Genesis, through the Civil War, World War II and right up to the present. Then I reveal the *why* and *when* and *how* of expressing your Ethical Will, followed by ways to help you develop a unique outline for your ethical message. Most importantly, I share a variety of inspiring and heartwarming examples of Ethical Wills. As you will see, many are—quite simply—extraordinary writing by ordinary people.

So, give yourself a gold star for even considering the task of creating and sharing a message of what you stand for and how you want to be remembered. I want to assure you that it's the first step of what will be a rewarding—and perhaps surprising—journey of self-discovery and sharing.

What makes *The Workshop Edition of SO GROWS THE TREE* unique

When I considered the wish list for *The Workshop Edition*, I wanted readers to have the advantage of a workshop environment at an affordable price even if there is no experienced workshop leader available to them. I also wanted to provide an audio book for those who are vision impaired or who would just rather listen than read. Because I can only be in so many places at once, the wish list also included sharing my slideshow presentation that brings alive the stories in *SO GROWS THE TREE*. Voila! *The Workshop Edition of SO GROWS THE TREE* wears several media hats:

It's a **book**, including the same text as the first edition of *SO GROWS THE TREE*.

It's a **workbook;** you can take notes on every page, there are lots of lined pages for musing, and every chapter includes thought-provoking questions and writing exercises to sharpen your creative skills.

It's a **workshop guide**, so you can share the experience of learning about and creating an Ethical Will with five or 500 of your closest friends. Instruction, expression and discussion are the elements of this Ethical Will workshop: a place where you can learn in an environment of encouragement, sharing and positive feedback.

It's a **slideshow**. The DVD in the back of the book is a narrated Powerpoint presentation picturing the faces, places, stories, examples and key elements of *The Workshop Edition of SO GROWS THE TREE,* along with the complete text, read by the author.

Finally, it's an **audio book** because you can just listen to the DVD. It follows the text of *SO GROWS THE TREE* word-for-word.

Advantages of the workshop approach

Even when experienced as a group, the journey to creating an Ethical Will consists of individuals travelling together. Because what you bring to the workshop is unique, your path will be different from that of your fellow travelers. The coming together of many diverse perspectives is part of what makes the workshop experience so worthwhile. Here are some other distinct advantages to workshopping:

1. **Discipline.** You are probably more likely to be at the appointed time and place when you know that others depend on your attendance and participation.

2. **Feedback.** We always learn from having others review our work and give their thoughtful critiques, and we learn even more from doing the same for them.

3. **Sharing ideas.** So many people, so many lives, so many perspectives—you're bound to hear something new and inspiring. Often our best ideas are born of another's casual comment.

4. **Encouragement.** Walking this journey with others is the opportunity to be instrumental in the creative process of many Ethical Wills. That's certainly a good thing!

5. **New friends.** Can a person really know *too* many people who want to review their core beliefs, aspire to the very best and share wisdom? Definitely not.

Recommendation for timing and structure of an Ethical Will workshop

I favor the following schedule for viewing the DVD and for workshopping:

- Watch the narrated slideshow in three Slideshow Sessions (the DVD is divided into three Slideshow Sessions and the book is divided into three corresponding Workshop Sessions). That will take about an hour each time. You can choose whether to read the chapters before viewing the DVD and whether to experience the Slideshow Sessions on your own or as a group.

- Gather after each Slideshow Session for the corresponding Workshop Session. To prepare, read the discussion questions and writing exercises ahead of time. If, like me, you are an over-preparer, go ahead and start jotting notes on the discussion questions or even start working on the writing exercises. Keeping in mind, of course, that workshopping is not a competitive sport!

- At each Workshop Session, first have someone read aloud the bulleted Review at the end of each chapter. Then go through as many of the corresponding discussion questions and writing exercises as you wish and as time allows.

- Ideally, each Workshop Session will be about two hours in length, including a break in the middle. There are recommended times for each writing exercise, but feel free to shorten or lengthen as you wish or even skip some discussion questions or exercises and spend more time on others. After all, it's *your* workshop.

- This approach to scheduling means that participants will be prepared to create an Ethical Will at the end of three two-hour Workshop Sessions. I recommend that Workshop Sessions be held weekly, so, at the end of three weeks, you will be ready—dare I say *eager*?—to start creating your own Ethical Will.

- Workshop participants may choose to continue to meet, perhaps monthly, to workshop their Ethical Wills-in-progress. Please try it at least once—it will encourage everyone to get a good start on their Ethical Wills, and it's fun and inspiring to share in the progress of others.

You choose how to use *The Workshop Edition of SO GROWS THE TREE*

Although some people prefer to work on their own and don't need or want the structure of a workshop, many others will find that experiencing *The Workshop Edition* process in a group makes the Ethical Will creation experience that much more rewarding.

The ultimate workshop experience consists of three Slideshow Sessions (about an hour for each Session) in which the narrated DVD is viewed on your own or gathered with others, and three Workshop Sessions (two hours each) where discussion, writing exercises and workshopping take place. But, *you* decide how you want to experience and use the features of *The Workshop Edition of SO GROWS THE TREE.*

On your own, using the workbook elements of the book:

1) Watch the narrated Slideshow Sessions and/or read the book.
2) Ponder the discussion questions at the end of each chapter.
3) Do the writing exercises that follow the discussion questions.
4) Create your Ethical Will.

In a group of a few or many, using the book as a workshop guide:

1) Experience the narrated Slideshow Sessions gathered with others or on your own.

2) Come together in Workshop Sessions for group discussion.

3) Do the writing exercises during the Workshop Sessions or between sessions as homework, or as a combination of both.

4) Workshop your writing as a group, sharing feedback on the exercises.

5) Create your Ethical Wills. You may decide to continue to meet on a regular basis to share the progress of your work after the workshop series has ended.

Or, design your own unique combination of methods. Here are two suggestions:

- On your own or in a group, watch the three narrated Slideshow Sessions all at once (they total a little over three hours) then cover each chapter's questions and writing exercises over a period of days or weeks, or

- As a group, watch the narrated slideshow for each chapter, followed immediately by the discussion questions and writing exercises for that chapter in a workshop setting.

A lot depends on how many people are sharing the experience and the length of time each person is willing and able to devote to the workshop (days, weeks or months). Remember: the goal of participating in an Ethical Will workshop is to ultimately create an Ethical Will, so choose the method that is most likely to encourage continued and enthusiastic participation by the members of the workshop.

Guidelines for conducting an Ethical Will workshop

Here are points to consider in putting together a workshop group and for making the most of this experience, especially if you have never been in a workshop before. These guidelines will help you organize and conduct a workshop with the least amount of stress and the fewest roadblocks to success.

Getting started. It's important that prospective attendees understand what an Ethical Will is when they receive your invitation to attend. In the *Appendix* chapter *The workshop facilitator's guide* on Page 141, you will find very specific assistance for the workshop organizer or facilitator, language for an e-mail invitation and even a flyer that you can copy and post or hand out to invitees.

Size of the group. Even partnering with one other person beats going it alone, and there isn't really a limit to the number of attendees. If you do decide to have a group of more than 20 persons, I suggest you break into smaller groups for discussion and workshopping segments.

Workshop location. The place where you hold your Workshop Sessions should be conducive to interaction and writing, so it's best to have tables and chairs although the book cover is designed to be its own writing surface, if necessary. Also, be sure seating is reasonably comfortable for the length of each session. Here are some suggestions:

- For small groups, a living room, dining room, family room or basement
- The meeting room of a church, fraternal organization or municipal building
- The dining room or activities room of a neighborhood senior center or retirement community

- A library meeting room, school classroom or auditorium
- The conference room of a business

Use your imagination. You can even meet outside, weather and locale permitting. Restroom facilities are a must.

Room setup. Ideally, the meeting place will allow for "banquet seating" where attendees are at round tables of 6-8 people. That not only provides a writing surface but it also encourages discussion because people are facing one another. If it is in a classroom, you may want to put desks or smaller tables in one or more circles. You can even sit in chairs without tables because the cover of *The Workshop Edition of SO GROWS THE TREE* acts as a hard writing surface.

Equipment. For individuals, the narrated slideshow DVD can be viewed on a television with a DVD player or on a desktop or laptop computer. If you are watching the Slideshow Sessions as a group, you'll want to make sure that all attendees are able to see and hear the presentation, so you will need one of these audio/visual setups:

- A big-screen television and DVD player or
- An LCD projector, laptop computer, screen and speakers.

Scheduling the Slideshow Sessions and Workshop Sessions. Ideally, mornings are the best time for learning, but schedule Slideshow Sessions and Workshop Sessions when most invitees are available and that may be evenings. If so, allow time for attendees to have a light dinner before the workshop begins.

Breaks. No matter how stimulating the subject, audience members of any age need a break once each hour, even if only a five minute stand-and-stretch. Attendees should always feel free to take a personal break whenever they need to. (It's easy to resume when you return: there is a numbered symbol like this 🎬#-# on each slide that corresponds to the 🎬#-# in the book.) Anytime you take a break, just pause the DVD and start it again when you are ready. Feel free to replay any part you want to hear again for clarification or just because you would like to repeat a passage in the narration.

Refreshments. No need to get fancy, but it would be nice to have a coffee pot going and a plate of cookies for breaks. You could suggest that each attendee bring his or her own beverage and a snack to share or, for a daytime workshop, schedule a brown bag or potluck break in the middle. And always be sure there is drinking water available.

Using the narrated slideshow DVD. The narration of the DVD slideshow follows this book exactly. That eliminates the need for note-taking—just sit back and enjoy the show! (One exception: if an image or words on the screen jog a memory or idea that you want to remember, make a note in the space provided on each page—later you'll be glad you did.) If you lose your place in the text, the numbered 🎬#-# symbols at the bottom of each slide match the numbered 🎬#-# symbols throughout the book. And remember, you have your own copy of the DVD, so you can watch it at home between group sessions or when the series is done if you want to review what you learned together as a group.

Discussion questions and writing exercises. There are no "right" or "wrong" answers to the discussion questions, so please offer input whenever you have something to contribute. As for the writing exercises, sometimes the muse is off duty and the words we seek just don't appear. However, I encourage you to write *something* each time because often that effort leads to the words you were hoping for.

Workshopping the writing exercises. You don't need to share your writing unless you wish to and there's no grade for class participation, but "workshopping" is the name of the game, so the more sharing and feedback that happens, the better.

An Ethical Will workshop is not a typical writers' workshop. Rather than working on a long-term writing project or even being published, the goals are to:

- *Acknowledge your beliefs and values, life lessons and hopes for the future.*
- *Create an Ethical Will that reveals the essence of what you stand for and how you want to be remembered.*
- *Set a tone and include examples and details that reinforce your message as well as give your loved ones a sense of your ethical spirit.*

Focus on the clarity of the message and its *ethical* essence, not its grammatical or literary essence. Remember that the role of the workshop attendees is much the same as that of the loved ones who will share any one of these Ethical Wills; it is invaluable to the creator of each Ethical Will to know whether the message being sent is the message being received. On Page 145 in the *Appendix*, there are more specific guidelines on workshopping but, as is true in most of life, the best rule for workshop etiquette is *The Golden Rule.*

Final thoughts on the workshop process. The principal advantage of a workshop environment is being able to share in the encouragement, imagination and feedback of others. Consider these points as you go forward:

- *The perspective you bring to an Ethical Will—your values, wisdom and hopes—is unique. It will affect you as a creator as well as a listener.*
- *From your fellow workshop attendees, you will learn something you did not know before: what "leaving a legacy of values" means to other persons.*
- *This Ethical Will workshop is another life lesson that will contribute to your own ethical footprint in some way, so keep your mind and heart open to the experience you are sharing and to the unique perspectives of your fellow travelers.*

As you begin your journey

I hope this innovative approach to creating an Ethical Will makes your journey of acknowledging, recording and sharing your beliefs and values, life lessons and hopes for the future more meaningful and effectual. Crafting the message of what you stand for and of how you want to be remembered will be a worthy and rewarding legacy for you as well as for your loved ones.

Homework assignment

I almost forgot! Take along a picture of a special occasion, place or memory in your life to the first Workshop Session. It might be a holiday, a vacation, a group of people or even an average scene in a lifetime of ordinary days. You will be sharing the picture with others only if you wish to.

There can be no vulnerability without risk;
there can be no community without vulnerability;
there can be no peace, and ultimately no life, without community.
M. Scott Peck

ᔥ Notes to Self ᔤ

No friendship can cross the path of our destiny
without leaving some mark on it forever.
François Mauriac

℘ Notes to Self ଔ

▰P-1 <u>WORKSHOP and SLIDESHOW SESSION I</u>

What you leave behind is not what is engraved in stone monuments,
but what is woven into the lives of others.
Pericles
▰P-2

▰P-3 ℬ Prelude ℭ

▰P-4 A 20-year-old stands in front of the Chicago & Northwestern Railroad office in Boone, Iowa. Hat in hand, he takes a deep breath, stands tall to make the most of his scant six foot build and opens the heavy oak door.

▰P-5 In the midst of a national post-war depression, Boone boasts a remarkably large population of 12,800 for the year 1921, mostly owing to its primary industry of coal: mining it and moving it. America's railway system has just been returned to private ownership after years of wartime nationalization. That explains the trains, lots and lots of trains. ▰P-6 This veteran of the First World War has come to apply for work as a railroad laborer. He is one of almost 4,000,000 "doughboys"[1] returning to civilian life and desperate to find a job.

▰P-7 His name is James Harold Godfred Kline,[2] my Uncle Bill. (His brother John Kline was called Uncle Frank, Aunt Winifred was really Susie Kline Sturtz and my father, Eugene Kline, was known as Uncle Dutch. The Klines are big on nicknames.) ▰P-8 Uncle Bill got that job, and after three years of advancing from laborer to baggageman to check clerk to yard clerk, he took a 15-month hiatus to attend Iowa State College (now Iowa State University) in Ames, Iowa and then returned to the railroad in December 1925 to resume his job as yard clerk. But that was just the beginning.

▰P-9 His career advanced in sync with the railroad industry: from Boone, Iowa to Clinton, Iowa to Madison, Wisconsin to Chicago, Illinois to Mason City, Iowa and ultimately to Marquette, Michigan in 1948. ▰P-10 Thirty-one years after starting as a laborer

Notes to Self

_____
_____
_____
_____
_____
_____
_____
_____
_____
_____
_____
_____
_____
_____
_____
_____
_____
_____
_____
_____
_____
_____

in Boone, Iowa, J. H. "Bill" Kline was named President of the Lake Superior & Ishpeming Railroad Co. on the shores of the Great Lakes' largest, Superior. When I think of Uncle Bill and Aunt Isabel,[3] I always think of their home and lifestyle in Marquette, Michigan.

🎬 P-11 Uncle Bill commanded a powerful presence. Obsessively hardworking and self-assured, he excelled as an industrial, political and civic leader. Aunt Isabel was the consummate homemaker and assumed the role of my uncle's partner in every sense with class and dignity. 🎬 P-12 Looking back, I now realize the commitment it must have taken in the 1950s and 1960s to keep these two branches of the Kline family so close; we had many unforgettable visits with them in Iowa and Michigan.

🎬 P-13 They both passed away in 1977, Uncle Bill suddenly and Aunt Isabel following a few months later. I remember them well and lovingly, and their place as icons in the Kline family is secure. So when I became the custodian of their personal papers and photos, I eagerly dug in, knowing that I would be uncovering some truly amazing stuff. And I did.

🎬 P-14 First was a black and white photo of four suited gentlemen, obviously taken sometime in the 1950s. Yes, that is definitely Jimmy Stewart and Otto Preminger; I recognize Uncle Bill as the one on the far right. 🎬 P-15 Then I remembered that the 1959 movie, *Anatomy of a Murder*, was filmed on location in Marquette and the Upper Peninsula. I'd adore that movie even if my Uncle Bill hadn't been involved with it, but it's even more captivating because he was. I looked at the premiere dinner program, autographed by every cast member and couldn't help but wonder what it might fetch on eBay.

🎬 P-16 I've always been a political junkie, regardless of the ebb and flow of my party affiliation, and in this box of manila folders and brown clasp envelopes was a time capsule of old-fashioned politics, a wealth of American artifacts from the cold war '50s and turbulent '60s, complete with campaign buttons and chicken dinner menus. ◀P-17 There was an autographed photo: "To Bill Kline with best wishes, Everett M. Dirksen, U.S. Senate." I recalled the Senator's famous quotation: "A million here, a million there. Pretty soon you're talking real money." ◀P-18 Uncle Bill had saved an appreciative letter from President Eisenhower after a fundraising event. A 1960 telegram from failed presidential candidate Richard Nixon lay atop a transcript of Uncle Bill's congressional testimony on the jeopardized future of the American rail system. Extraordinary souvenirs were uncovered, one after another. I was, as we Iowans say, in hog heaven.

Mementoes of Uncle Bill's business life had been preserved as well. ◀P-19 An employee had written a poem about "The Boss" for Uncle Bill's retirement party. There were congratulatory letters received when he took the job as railroad president and countless well wishes prompted by his decision to retire. I was barely an adult when my uncle passed away. ◀P-20 Now, through each piece of memorabilia, I received an unexpected glimpse of the person I had revered but never really known: Uncle Bill as seen through the eyes of those outside the family.

And then, among the invaluable ephemera representing a lifetime of public and professional service, I found the truly priceless treasure tucked away in that box.

◀P-21 At first glance, it looked just like any other letter. It was the 1960s—we wrote letters. We wrote letters when we went away to camp, to college, on vacation and every other week of the year. Communication options were limited: long distance phone calls were a luxury reserved for national holidays and the announcement of an unexpected death; e-mail was 40 years in the future. This was one of countless letters that had passed from one sibling to another, between my Uncle Bill and his brother, my father Eugene.

But this was not just like any other letter. It was written by my uncle one week before his retirement on Thursday, March 28, 1963. And it was a letter that my father had kept for 20 years until his own death in September 1982.

Thursday – 28th

Dear Gene –

It now looks like our winter is on the way out. Snow has been melting for more than a week.

I would like to suggest that you try some of the theraphy that I use, both physical and mental. For sometime I have been completely convinced that exercise is one of the best tranquilizers and for a person of your age and mine the best exercise is walking. I attempt to follow a schedule of walking from forty minutes to one hour every day. I have been doing this for about eighteen months. I can truthfully say I walk briskly with ease, without discomfort and that includes the hills around here. Actually, I can walk as well as I did twenty-five years ago and with a lot less puffing. This walking should be done with complete freedom of thought. Dispel all thoughts of business and home. Concentrate on everything observed.

Physical theraphy is important but it is no more so than mental theraphy. Our mental attitudes are so closely associated with our feelings and overall well being. The assertion "open mind" is often made. But its true meaning and importance is rarely understood. It's true meaning is the mind is "open". That is, not cluttered with prejudices, ill feelings, vindictive thinking and "get even" threats. An open mind must be objective. One must first think positively, eliminating all negative conclusions. Think briefly about people you know who react negatively to everything. Do you recall one who was happy and well balanced? They can not be because they must be constantly on guard to continue their unco-operative attitude. Every problem has a solution and it can be found if the proper consideration is given to all the factors.

Consideration of the opinion of others is all important. All too often we quickly decide that what someone says or believes is ridiculous, childish or completely incompetent. We must remember that he is entitled to his opinion as we are and has a right to express himself. I do not agree with many people but I try to respect their opinion and not be upset about it. Voltaire once said, "I may violently disagree with what you say but I will defent to the death your right to say it".

We should also be more tolerant to accept the things going on about us. Remember, world history has been going on for thousands of years, and the factors involving our daily lives have been building up for many lifetimes. I think the following prayer illustrates this quite well: "May God grant me the serenity to accept the things I cannot change; the courage to change the things I can; and the wisdom to know the difference".

I know I am not much of a relifious man but I am convinced that one should constantly seek Devine Guidance. It is truly amazing how you will feel that your supplications are answered.

This is my last week at the office so from now on can work for myself—or can I?

Always,
Bill[4]

It was one of the first Ethical Wills I ever read, although I didn't realize it at the time. As surely as if he had known that I would someday be on this mission to learn and teach about Ethical Wills and their timeless value, Uncle Bill had left his own to be discovered by me.

I read it and re-read it. Minor grammatical errors aside, it was flawless. There was not a single strike-over or visible correction. Had he outlined his thoughts before typing? The no-nonsense businessman and stalwart conservative was quoting Voltaire and reciting *The Serenity Prayer*. Is it possible that this letter was the product of serendipitous inspiration, surfacing as he sat at the typewriter? Clearly, my father had sensed its importance; he had singled out this one of many letters and he had stowed it for safekeeping in a box marked simply "Bill & Isabel," to be discovered and treasured by me 25 years after his death.[5]

Perhaps Uncle Bill was just musing, having a reflective moment after a day of packing up his office, simply giving his baby brother the benefit of his senior years of dealing with life's confounding turns. Of them, he knew more than a little. ▰P-22 He and my Aunt Isabel had lost their only child, my cousin Mary Kathryn, in a commercial airline crash just four months before he wrote this letter.[6] She was a 22-year-old with a dazzling smile, a sophisticated air and a determined spirit. She had been the epicenter of their lives and the depth of their grief and loss was immeasurable. Yes, considering the context of his message, I'd say my Uncle Bill knew as much about keeping one's head above life's waters as any human could stand to know.

In this letter, this Ethical Will, Uncle Bill had generously bequeathed his time-tested coping mechanisms and life philosophies. Like his persona, direct and plainspoken, he offered up the simplest of approaches to the most complex of life's challenges and delivered it all with no shortage of conviction.

▰P-23 Uncle Bill had recorded his Ethical Will, this poignant message of his beliefs and values, life lessons and hopes for the future, and he had taken the second important step: he had shared it with a loved one. I doubt if he expected the audience to extend past my father, and surely he never imagined this letter as part of a book written 47 years later. 📽P-24 *But that's how it is with Ethical Wills: you never really know who might be touched by your message sometime in the future.*

📽P-25 Simply put, an Ethical Will is one's personal mission statement. It is an expression of the most important and unique part of each of us: what we stand for. It can be a simple handwritten letter or a video miniseries. You can make a one-page list of favorite quotations or songs and why each rings true to you, or you can log every childhood memory you count as significant and tell others why.

📽P-26 In the coming chapters I share the story of Ethical Wills, from their beginning more than 35 centuries ago to their contemporary resurgence, and why they play an important role in weaving the moral fiber of a society. Most importantly, I show you how easy it is to create an Ethical Will, and I encourage you to join with those throughout history—famous and otherwise—who have taken the time to share their thoughts, to record the guiding principles of their lives, to create their Ethical Wills.

📽P-27 *Feel free to jot on the "Notes to Self" spaces or in the margins whenever your muse visits: a quotation, a story, a memory, a snippet or a mental snapshot that might make a valuable addition to your message. And before we go on, put your name in the front of this book where it says* 📽P-28 *"This book belongs to _____." Do it because this book is my view on how best to create and share an Ethical Will, but—make no mistake—it's <u>your</u> story.*

End of the Prelude
📽P-29

To live in hearts we leave behind is not to die.
Thomas Campbell

✼ Notes to Self ✼

How we spend our days is, of course,
how we spend our lives.
Annie Dillard

ℰ **Notes to Self** ℛ

p 133 list

▄1-1 Part I.
Everything you need to know about Ethical Wills

The only thing to do with good advice is to pass it on.
It is never any use to oneself.
Oscar Wilde
▄1-2

▄1-3 ଗ Chapter One ର
The Greatest Story: the first Ethical Will
(What is an Ethical Will?)

What is an Ethical Will? ▄1-4 It's what you believe, what you know and what you hope for.

▄1-5 Think of someone you know well, someone you admire and consider a friend. Imagine describing that person using only three words. Choose carefully. ▄1-6 It is not an easy assignment, but when you are done, you will have captured the essence of that person, what he or she stands for, what first comes to mind when you think of that person.

▄1-7 Complete the exercise again but describe yourself this time. ▄1-8 Deepen the meaning with examples, stories from a lifetime of experiences and thoughts of what you hope the future will bring and—voila!—you have created your Ethical Will, the essence of what you stand for.

An Ethical Will has three essential elements:

▄1-9 **Beliefs and values.**   These are the core values and principles that have served you well throughout your life. They consistently prove to be trustworthy and to operate as a reliable moral compass, no matter what the trial or circumstances. *Character, principles, reputation, integrity, life philosophy, ideals, credo.*

▄1-10 **Life lessons.** Life lessons are the principles you know to be true that are learned in just one place: the School of Hard Knocks. *Experience, stories, reflections, observations, advice, wisdom.*

▄1-11 **Hopes for the future.** The world tomorrow will not be the same as today—that's for sure. Your Ethical Will is the place to hope for the best and the opportunity to envision a future where all the wishes for you and for those you love come true. Nothing can exist until it is first imagined. *Dreams, aspirations, objectives, goals, wishes.*

Notes to Self

_____

_____

_____

_____

_____

_____

_____

_____

_____

_____

_____

_____

_____

_____

_____

_____

_____

_____

_____

I used the expression ▰1-12 "personal mission statement" a little earlier. For a business or organization, the mission statement defines its purpose and what it aspires to be. When faced with a potential product, direction or service, the shareholders or members should first refer to the mission statement to verify that the proposed venture fits within the parameters of the corporate philosophy.

An Ethical Will does much the same for an individual and acts as an ethical blueprint on a personal level for the author and for those who share his or her Ethical Will. More expansive than the one- or two-phrase paragraph of a corporate mission statement, an Ethical Will can come alive with stories, examples, quotations, recipes, experiences or pictures. It expresses the individuality of each person, what makes your message one-of-a-kind and uniquely meaningful.

▰1-13 The history of Ethical Wills

▰1-14 Fifteen hundred years before the birth of Christ, surrounded by his twelve sons and their children, lies Jacob, son of Isaac and Rebecca, grandson of Abraham and Sarah. He is dying. As recorded in the Old Testament Book of Genesis, Jacob took this opportunity to share his beliefs, the lessons he had learned throughout his own life and his hopes for his sons:

> Then Jacob called his sons, and said, Gather yourselves together, that I may tell you what shall befall you in days to come. Assemble and hear, O sons of Jacob and hearken to Israel your father.[7]

This oral blessing from Jacob on the brink of his death is one of the first known Ethical Wills. Jacob's spoken message was recorded in the Hebrew Bible some 100 years after his death. Much later, in 1050 A.D., the earliest example of a written Ethical Will appeared.[8] ▰1-15 The following example from 1357 A.D. is the quintessential Ethical Will, a straight-forward guide for living an ethical life from Eleazar the Levite of Mainz :

> Judge every man charitably, and use your best efforts to find a kindly explanation of conduct, however suspicious... Give in charity an exact tithe of your property. Never turn a poor man away empty-handed. Talk no more than is necessary, and thus avoid slander. Be not as dumb cattle that utter no word of gratitude, but thank God for his bounties at the time at which they occur, and in your prayers let the memory of these personal favors warm your hearts and prompt you to special fervor during the utterance of the communal thanks for communal well-being. When words of

thanks occur in the liturgy, pause and silently reflect on the goodness of God to you that day.[9]

🎬1-16 The audience for an ancient Ethical Wills was limited to the children of an aging father or the pupils of an elder teacher, and Ethical Wills were "...for the most part written calmly in old age..."[10] Thankfully, the tradition ultimately expanded. 🎬1-17 Anne Dudley Bradstreet, the first published poet of the New World (1650 Massachusetts), penned a moving letter, "To My Dear Children," at age 44, which is prefaced with this simple rhyme,

> 🎬1-18 *This book by any yet unread,*
> *I leave for you when I am dead.*
> *That being gone, here you may find*
> *What was your living mother's mind.*
> *Make use of what I leave in love,*
> *And God shall bless you from above.*
> *A. B.*

In it she speaks eloquently of the life lessons of her childhood and motherhood and her life-long and deep, although oft-tested, faith.[11]

🎬1-19 A letter written by Major Sullivan Ballou just before his death at the Civil War battle of Bull Run in 1861 is another unintended Ethical Will. 🎬1-20 Meant for his wife Sarah, but never mailed, it was penned just a week before his death. Like so many other "last letters" from so many other wars, Major Ballou's letter is more than just a recitation of his love for his family; it is an acknowledgement of destiny and an affirmation of the value known as patriotism.

> 🎬1-21 *I have no misgivings about, or lack of confidence in, the cause in which I am engaged, and my courage does not halt or falter. I know how strongly American Civilization now leans upon the triumph of the Government, and how great a debt we owe to those who went before us through the blood and suffering of the Revolution. And I am willing—perfectly willing—to lay down all my joys in this life, to help maintain this Government and to pay that debt.*[12]

🎬1-22 Contemporary examples of Ethical Wills were spawned from the horror of the Holocaust as the imprisoned scratched out messages, fighting to make memorable their abbreviated lives and imminent deaths. In describing these written legacies, the authors of *So That Your Values Live On—Ethical Wills and How to Prepare Them*, put it so well:

1-23 Some demand vengeance and a continuing fight to the death with the cruel oppressor and all that he represents. Others, to our everlasting wonder, reveal a struggle to maintain the author's divine image and human dignity in the face of incomparable evil.[13]

1-24 If these writings had simply addressed the daily hardships of life for the colonists or the front line suffering of a Civil War soldier or the horrendous details of life in a concentration camp, respectively, they would still be significant writings, but they would not be mentioned in this book. What makes each historical perspective an Ethical Will is the author's insistence on sharing the values, hard-earned wisdom and hopes that were formed or revealed in each grueling situation.

Whether motivated by the hardships of life or impending death, Ethical Wills throughout history are heartfelt messages that maintain their relevance no matter how remote in time the author's life may be.

1-25 The here and now of Ethical Wills

Throughout history, Ethical Wills have been widely used although not widely known. 1-26 Jacob and his later historical contemporaries have been joined by Abraham Lincoln, Ralph Waldo Emerson, Mark Twain, John Wayne, Randy Pausch, Tim Russert and countless others in crafting enduring messages of what they believed, what they knew and what they hoped for. 1-27 Credit the ubiquitous Baby Boomers for the renaissance of this tradition. With so many people reaching and surpassing middle age, it's no wonder the thought of recording one's message—a look at one's life in the rearview mirror—has gained in popularity and practice. Like Gerber®, Barbie® and the Hula Hoop®, the simple act of one person multiplied by 78,000,000 causes a cultural tsunami. Ethical Wills are most definitely back in style.

1-28 You will see that an Ethical Will tells us more about the writer than its mere words convey. Its very existence speaks to the person's willingness—perhaps even obsession—to share his or her thoughts on the meaning of life, or at least one life. Unlike legal documents prepared by an attorney to specify one's wishes for medical care at life's end or the distribution of one's assets,[14] an Ethical Will is typically drafted by an amateur writer. It is an expression of beliefs liberally sprinkled with uniquely personal feelings. 1-29 Simple or arcane, Ethical Wills have been and will always be examples of extraordinary writing, even when created by ordinary people.

▰1-30 *An Ethical Will is your philosophical and spiritual essence,* ▰1-31 *reflecting what you believe in, what you know to be true and what you hope will come to be with the passage of time. Whether labeled a legacy letter, a spiritual will, an ending note, a personal mission statement, a philosophical journal,[15] a vision statement, a bequest of values or a love letter, the underlying principle of an Ethical Will is always the same:* ▰1-32 *"This is how I want to be remembered."*

End of Chapter One
▰1-33

Review - Chapter One
- An Ethical Will is the summary of your beliefs and values, life lessons and hopes for the future.
- One of the first known Ethical Wills was Jacob's message to his twelve sons just before his death, as recorded in the Bible's Book of Genesis.
- We have examples of Ethical Wills throughout history: from the Middle Ages, the Civil War, the Holocaust and contemporary times.

Ponder this...
Questions for discussion

1. Do you have any examples of an Ethical Will in your own life or in your family history? _____

2. Have you ever written or created something similar to an Ethical Will? _____
_____

3. Have you ever received an Ethical Will from someone else? What has it meant to you? _____

4. If you know, what were the circumstances that lead the person to create that Ethical Will? _____

5. Can you think of examples of writing (famous or not) that you now recognize as Ethical Wills? _____
_____
_____
_____
_____
_____
_____

*The harvest of old age is the memory
and rich story of blessings laid up earlier in life.*
Cicero

❧ Notes to Self ☙

We don't learn from experience.
We learn from reflecting on experience.
John Dewey
🎬2-1

🎬2-2 ഔ **Chapter Two** ଔ
As the twig is bent, so grows the tree
(Why create an Ethical Will?)

🎬2-3 The poet Alexander Pope lived at the turn of the eighteenth century. He was a singularly unattractive man, mocked for his four-foot-six-inch frame and humpback, the legacy of contracting tuberculosis at the age of twelve. He might have been just another poor soul who lived an unremarkable life of ridicule but for his prodigious output of critical prose and poetry, often fashioned in a snarky sort of way. Most importantly, few writers can boast the reams of quotations that have long survived Alexander Pope.[16]

Even if you are not a literary scholar—which I most certainly am not, although I have the good sense to occasionally hang out with others who are—you can recognize his work in many well-known and oft-repeated quotations. To list just a few: 🎬2-4

"Fools rush in where angels fear to tread."

"Hope springs eternal in the human breast."

"A little learning is a dangerous thing."

"To err is human; to forgive, divine."

(Bear with me—it was a meandering journey to the title of this book but worth your time to look back with me.) 🎬2-5 As I studied ancient and modern examples of Ethical Wills, it became obvious that the message of an Ethical Will can, intentionally or otherwise, reach far beyond the space and time of its initial audience, the writer's chosen circle of loved ones. Especially in writing this chapter, I thought a lot about how to best make you, the reader, appreciate the potential impact of a scant few well-chosen words.

Take, for instance, the amazing kismet of my 🎬2-6 Uncle Bill's Ethical Will traveling to me over the decades. The contents of his letter are thought-provoking and inspirational to me and for each Kline family member who reads it. As important, though, is the lesson of its very existence: J. H. "Bill" Kline's Ethical Will demonstrates the vast difference between relying on fuzzy

Notes to Self

_____

_____

_____

_____

_____

_____

_____

_____

_____

_____

_____

_____

_____

_____

_____

_____

_____

_____

_____

_____

memories and suppositions about a person's beliefs, values and wisdom and having the real deal, spelled out by him or her.

2-7 If you've been bitten by the genealogy bug, you know all about family trees and the many formats now available to diagram your ancestors and descendants. There are fan charts, pedigree charts, descendant charts, bowtie charts, ancestor charts, hourglass charts, and charts that look like real trees, if real trees had gilded leaves. After you input all the place, birth, marriage, divorce, remarriage, children, grandchildren and death data, it's darn satisfying to see it laid out in a neat pictorial.

Now step back and view that family tree as more than just a trunk of grandparents with branches of aunts and uncles and scores of first cousin twigs and first-cousins-once-or-more-removed leaves. 2-8 More than simply a way to organize one's genealogy, a family tree symbolizes the propagation of a belief system, a way of approaching life, a means of measuring one's contribution to society and appreciating how the seemingly remote journeys of others have influenced our own.

The seeds of my grandparents, John and Hannah (Smith) Kline, married on October 16, 1892, have proliferated to over 150 descendants as of the publication of this book (at last count there are 32 twigs and over 107 leaves). 2-9 To be quite honest and not at all self-deprecating, a glance around the picnic tables at a Kline family reunion reveals the collective themes of hard work and the importance of education. We are bright, ambitious, funny, self-assured, driven, dogmatic, opinionated, passionate and a touch obsessive—each and every trait epitomized in an endearing, albeit occasionally overbearing, manner. All this praise by way of saying that there is a common thread, *something* that makes us uniquely Klines, as can be said of every family, for the good, bad or nondescript. By mandate or example, the members come to know the standards for acceptable and objectionable conduct that form the core beliefs and values of each family.

2-10 Now, multiply that family unit by 114 million[17] and ponder how we formulate and preserve the beliefs, ethics and principles of an entire nation. It's not by happenstance, that's for sure. A culture's moral compass is the direct reflection of the attitudes and actions of its constituents, and we perpetuate what we stand for as a nation by the daily words and deeds of 300 million individuals, the members of our societal "family." If our communal value system—our laws and our nation's moral compass—shifts in such a way that our civility is diminished, we need look no further than our kitchen tables and our one-on-one social interactions to find the source.

🎬2-11 It's a bit like an ethical Butterfly Effect: tiny changes in a system (the flapping of a butterfly's wings) can ultimately result in a large-scale effect (a tornado).[18] Although it is sometimes difficult to admit, the laws of our nation *do* reflect our core values and society's principles *are* personified in millions of daily examples and declarations. Don't just take my word for it:

🎬2-12 *"I hope that the foundation of our national policy will be laid in the pure and immutable principles of private morality."*   - George Washington

🎬2-13 *"There is seldom an instance of a man guilty of betraying his country, who had not before lost the feeling of moral obligations in his private connections."*
                    - Samuel Adams

🎬2-14 *"Bad men cannot make good citizens. A vitiated state of morals, a corrupted pubic conscience are incompatible with freedom."*   - Patrick Henry

🎬2-15 *"Before any man can be considered as a member of Civil Society, he must be considered as a subject of the Governor of the Universe."*   - James Madison

🎬2-16 *"The only foundation of a free Constitution is pure Virtue, and if this cannot be inspired into our People in a greater Measure than they have it now, they may change their Rulers and the forms of Government, but they will not obtain a lasting liberty."*   - John Adams

🎬2-17 *"When we are planning for posterity, we ought to remember that virtue is not hereditary."*   – Thomas Paine

🎬2-18 Simply put, *E pluribus unum* means *Out of many, one.* It was the strongly-held belief of the Founding Fathers, the men who crafted the 🎬2-19 Constitution and the Bill of Rights, that it would take a constant and concentrated effort on the part of the citizenry to maintain the free republic they had toiled to establish. Although the founding fathers believed that the destiny of the United States was divinely ordained, 🎬2-20 they also considered the documents enumerating our guiding principles to be just that: guiding—but not supernatural. They were neither cynical nor naïve about our human tendency to stray from the path of righteousness and stated forthrightly that patriotism would not survive in the absence of integrity. The Founding Fathers were very wise.

▰2-21 Practicing what you stand for on a daily basis is what true character is all about. When you record your core beliefs by creating an Ethical Will, you take an important leap: you share and bequeath your perspective on life, a vision that will influence your circle of loved ones, and, in turn, those whom *they* influence, today and perhaps for thousands of tomorrows.

And so it was that my eyes fell on this Alexander Pope quotation at the same time I was considering all these family tree, space/time continuum concepts:

▰2-22 *"'Tis education forms the common mind.*
Just as the twig is bent, the tree's inclined."

Or, as it is more commonly spoken,

"As the twig is bent, so grows the tree."

▰2-23 If you visit our home in the Christmas season, be prepared to watch *It's a Wonderful Life.* Its timeless message: the value of one person's existence can only be measured by extrapolating to all the lives he or she touches in countless ways every day, known and unsuspected. Likewise, Alexander Pope's stock went up a tick when his words travelled successfully over two hundred fifty years to become the title of this book.

▰2-24 You can speak your mind—and you should, loudly and often—but your Ethical Will gives a permanence to what you stand for. There is a legitimacy, a well-deserved reverence, for words and for a tradition fashioned from them that have survived for more than 3,500 years and continue to evolve today. Creating an Ethical Will is claiming your spot in the long line of those who appreciate the importance of crafting, sharing and living one's message of core beliefs. This simple act cements your place as a brick in the foundation of a country as well as a family. ▰2-25 And *that's* why this book is called *SO GROWS THE TREE.*

▰2-26 Reasons to create an Ethical Will

The perception of "legacy" is an interesting topic. ▰2-27 So compelling, in fact, that the folks at The Allianz Life Insurance Company of North America decided to survey public opinion on it. It seems that when you ask Baby Boomers and their parents to rank how important it is to receive or provide different types of inheritance, only 10 percent of Baby Boomers think it's very important to receive financial assets or real estate from their parents. In sharp contrast, 39 percent of the parents ranked those same hard assets as "very important."

⛶2-28 But ask both demographic groups about receiving and providing *values and life lessons* and they are 100 percent in agreement: 77 percent of Baby Boomers and 77 percent of their parents think it is *very important* to receive and pass on, respectively, the legacy of what you believe and what you know— more important than to receive and pass on financial assets or real estate.[19] Who knew?

⛶2-29 So why create an Ethical Will? The answer is simple: because you can. You have a message you want to share, and most likely there's someone out there who wants to hear it. The simple impulse to share one's stories and wisdom is the most common reason someone considers creating an Ethical Will. That's probably part of what motivated you to pick up this book. However, in the process of organizing and creating, you will find that there are other, perhaps unforeseen, reasons for and benefits from creating your Ethical Will.

why write?

⛶2-30 Self-reflection

Before you can record your core beliefs and values in your Ethical Will, you have to know what they are. Composing your Ethical Will requires you to think—really think—about what you have been, are, and hope to be, character-wise: your ethical essence. It's a chance to give yourself a well-deserved pat on the back (assuming you deserve one). Another fringe benefit of doing some mental homework before choosing the words to create your Ethical Will is that thinking about ⛶2-31 what we stand for *now* can lead us to think about what we *hope* to stand for. More about aspirations later.

ethical essence

⛶2-32 Sharing core beliefs and values

As the entrepreneur Frank Rooney said: ⛶2-33 *"Immortality is the genius to move others long after you have stopped moving."* Back to the goal of preserving our communal character: the best way to be sure your message lives on after you is to put it in writing. It may be read by only your close family members or it may make its way into a book such as this one 50 years from now. Either way, an Ethical Will is your chance to memorialize your opinion on the most important aspects of living and point out which parts of your daily life really make a difference in the big scheme of things.

⛶2-34 Storytelling

Perhaps less factual than an autobiography, a memoir relates life's most significant events and focuses on their meaning from the perspective of the observer, the writer. Strictly speaking, your life story is not an Ethical Will, but if you include your reflections on the values, lessons and hopes that you gained from key events, you will be combining the storytelling of an autobiography with the core elements of an Ethical Will. In such an Ethical Will/mini memoir, you can see how storytelling plays an important role. A little later I talk about 🎬2-35 Ethical Eulogies, Ethical Tributes and Ethical Genealogy. Each is an opportunity to tell stories about another person while sharing the value system that makes him or her unique. And that can be done even if you've never had the privilege of meeting the main character of the tale. Living history. Yes, there's definitely a place for storytelling in Ethical Wills.

🎬2-36 Reconciliation

Never to be confused with *recrimination*, an Ethical Will can be the best place to ask for or grant forgiveness, if you want to and are unable to do so face-to-face. When you focus on what is most important in your life and in your relationships, you may recognize incidents that have earned undeserved importance such as a past wrong or grudge. As you identify your core values, you may choose to put the message of your Ethical Will to practical use and restore a broken relationship while you are both still here to enjoy it.

ask for forgiveness

🎬2-37 Future aspirations

Life is a series of transitions: birth, death, divorce, separation, empty-nesting, career changes, a serious or chronic illness, retirement. Whether a time to count blessings or to mourn a loss, each and every one is an opportunity to gain and perhaps share wisdom.

There is no need to wait until the end of life is peeking 'round the corner to create your Ethical Will. Recording your personal message any time prior to The End forces you to not only reflect on past lessons but also identify new goals going forward. Reviewing values and life lessons leads you to contemplate and itemize the "hope for" part of your Ethical Will: 🎬2-38 your "ethical bucket list." They are the standards you want to maintain and the ideals you hope to achieve. Much like a corporate mission statement, an Ethical Will provides the author with a lifelong blueprint for the daily practice of beliefs and values.

ethical bucket list

writing your personal message help to identify new goals

🎬2-39 Estate planning and Footprint Philanthropy™

Although The Allianz American Legacies Study shed light on the importance of giving and receiving *values and life lessons* as an important element of one's "legacy," it is not inappropriate to ponder how the passing on of money or property also helps to make the world a better place. Your "footprint" may be material as well as ethical.

🎬2-40 **Personal bequests.** You have probably thought about who you want to remember in your estate plan, even if you have not yet determined your level of generosity. Regardless of your ultimate choices, using the outline of an Ethical Will may help you

Ethical Will is like adding your voice to otherwise sterile, matter-of-fact legal documents.

▄2-46 An end-of-life Ethical Will

▄2-47 As Kay Lyons said, *"Yesterday is a cancelled check; tomorrow is a promissory note; today is the only cash you have—so spend it wisely."*[22] As you will discover, creating an Ethical Will is a valuable spiritual exercise at any time in life, but it has special significance when the end is near. Being mindful as life ends is an opportunity to appreciate the impermanence of life and to cherish and fully experience each remaining moment. I spoke earlier of the beneficial self-reflection that comes from creating an Ethical Will. Experiencing a mindful death is more of the same: being present in the moment, acknowledging and processing the intense emotions and physical changes that surround letting go.

When death is imminent, bereavement for the end of life and the loss of key relationships envelopes the dying person and the loved ones at his or her side. The creation of an Ethical Will at the end of life, by or on behalf of the dying person, is more than just a desperate game of beat-the-clock, the last chance to record important thoughts and feelings. It is a valuable tool in acknowledging and seeing beyond the physiology of dying by focusing on the person's essence and the meaning and value of his or her life on Earth, whatever time may remain. And it can be key to not missing one bit of life, even though moments may be numbered.[23]

▄2-48 **Saying goodbye.** The emotions of the dying patient and loved ones may be in turmoil as death approaches: impending loss, regrets, grief, anger, confusion, panic, fear, and fatigue, to name a few. It may be difficult, if not impossible, to identify and verbalize those feelings. Often putting one's emotions in writing is less daunting, permitting them to be acknowledged, communicated and validated.

Perspective. Reviewing one's life and all it has meant helps the dying patient and loved ones more easily see the circle of life and more vividly appreciate the patient's vital role in it as a living person and as an inspiring memory as life goes on for those left behind.

Acceptance. Anyone who has suffered the loss of a loved one knows that although *closure* is an unattainable goal, *peace* may be. An Ethical Will may aid in acknowledging mortality, an important step in preparing for the approaching end of life, allowing the greatest appreciation of whatever time remains for both the patient and the survivors.

Autonomy and control. Dying patients often feel they no longer have control of their lives. Aspiring to experience a mindful death and recording one's Ethical Will shows the patient that he or she continues to be in charge, no matter how little time may be left.

The values and beliefs identified in a dying person's Ethical Will can be priceless guidance for loved ones as they struggle to let go. If allowing the dying patient to plan for his or her own funeral or memorial is possible, incorporating the elements of an Ethical Will makes those plans personal, meaningful and more likely to be honored by survivors.

Blueprint for hospice care. When curing the disease is no longer an option, the focus of health care professionals, caregivers, loved ones and the patient should turn to nurturing a mindful death, at all times maintaining respect for the wishes of the dying person. Hospice care is a medical discipline that focuses on the comfort of, and respect for, a patient nearing the end of life. It centers on honoring the patient's wishes for dignity and peace, where and how final days will be spent and who should be present. Assisting a dying person to express stories and wisdom in an Ethical Will can serve as guidance for health care professionals seeking to respect that patient's unique essence at life's end.

2-49 Reasons to create an Ethical Will—*not!*

2-50 The first Ethical Will, recorded in the Book of Genesis, has a certain amount of finger-pointing sprinkled among the blessings. If you read Jacob's blessing in full, you'll see that it did not bode all that well for two of his sons, Simeon and Levi, and his prophecy for Benjamin's life was less than optimistic.[24] 2-51 This brings us to a guiding principle for writing an effective Ethical Will: *reconciliation* is good; *recrimination* not so much.

Your Ethical Will is the wrong place to stick it to those left behind. Consider the potential longevity of your Ethical Will and guard that the energy, the essence, the legacy of your message is affirming as well as long-lived. If you have a gripe to settle with another person, best to do so while you are both still breathing and can benefit from any remaining time spent at peace with each other. If that is not practical, possible or desirable, let go and move on without the baggage.

Contrary to Jacob's example, I suggest you leave out the venting and guilt trip guided tours. Think about it: Do you really want your great-great-grandchildren to know you best by your ability to cut to the quick with a few well-placed harsh words? 2-52 Just a suggestion...

It's almost impossible to imagine the world without you in it, isn't it? 2-53 *And yet, the day will come when every person now reading this book—and yes, that includes the author—will no longer inhabit the Earth. You have the opportunity to craft a message that will reflect your philosophical essence and leave little doubt as to* 2-54 *what you believed, learned and hoped for, even after you are gone. Part of your legacy is your Ethical Will.*

End of Chapter Two
▰ 2-55
Review - Chapter Two

Reason (handwritten margin note)

- Our cultural value systems are formulated and preserved by our attitudes and actions as individuals. These core beliefs guide our families, communities and nation and have since the time of our Founding Fathers.

- When surveyed, Baby Boomers and their parents agree that the most important "inheritance" is the receipt and gift of values and life lessons.

- Among the reasons to create an Ethical Will are self-reflection, sharing core beliefs and values, storytelling, reconciliation, future aspirations, estate planning and Footprint Philanthropy™, as a blueprint for end-of-life planning, and as a guide for the final chapter of life.

- An Ethical Will is best not used for finger-pointing or recrimination.

why write? (handwritten margin note)

Ponder this...
Questions for discussion

Question (handwritten margin note)

1. Have you thought about your own motivations for creating an Ethical Will? If so, what are they? _____

_____

_____

_____

2. Which of these reasons to create an Ethical Will appeals most to you? Why?
Self-reflection
Sharing core beliefs and values ✓
Story-telling
Reconciliation
Future aspirations
Estate planning and Footprint Philanthropy™
Blueprint for end-of-life planning
An end-of-life Ethical Will ✓

_____

_____

_____

_____

_____

_____

_____

_____

_____

3. Can you identify the core beliefs and values of your immediate family? _____

   hard work, responsibility, Independence _____

   _____

4. Looking back, can you identify the ways in which those beliefs and values were expressed and enforced in your family? *rewarded support* _____

   _____

5. Have you observed any change in the core values of your community over your lifetime? Can you share an example? _____

   _____

Now, let's exercise our creativity...
Chapter Two - Exercise 1

Choose one of the following reasons to create an Ethical Will and write just three sentences—sort of a mini-Ethical Will—that demonstrate one or more of your values.

Self-reflection
Sharing core beliefs and values
Storytelling
Reconciliation
Future aspirations
Estate planning and Footprint Philanthropy™
Blueprint for end-of-life health care planning
Sharing your message at the end of life

3 sentences
that reflect your values

Example:
"Blueprint for end-of-life health care planning"
One of my core values is accountability and being responsible for my actions.
I have observed while caring for others at the end of their lives that independence is a vital part of maintaining a sense of self.
I hope my family will consider the quality *of my life as well as the* quantity *of my days if they have to make health care or end-of-life decisions on my behalf.*

Now, it's your turn (suggested: 10 minutes/3 sentences) _____

_____

_____

_____

_____

_____

_____

_____

_____

_____

_____

Chapter Two - Exercise 2

You brought the picture of a special occasion, place or memory with you. Look closely at the place or at the faces of the people pictured there. What is it about that scene that makes you think of your family's values—the standards that make your family unique? Write about 100 words on the core values or characteristics of your family that come to mind.

Example:

My father's family, The Klines, are known for being hardworking and hardplaying. When I look at this picture, I remember like yesterday being with my ginormous group of cousins at a reunion or Christmas gathering at my Aunt Winifred and Uncle Dewey's home, seeing some family members just that one time each year, but using that time to keep in touch with each others' lives and never-changing personalities. The homes we came from were so different: some from the farm, some from small towns, some from big cities, near and far. And yet we have always been tethered by a common thread: shared ancestors, shared history and shared memories.

Now, it's your turn (suggested: 10 minutes/100 words) _____

Lives of great men all remind us
we can make our lives sublime, and departing,
leave behind us footprints in the sand of time.
Henry Wadsworth Longfellow
🎬 3-1

🎬 3-2 ᔕᔓ **Chapter Three** ᘓᘔ
Raise your hand if you have a story to share
(Who creates an Ethical Will?)

🎬3-3 When I am speaking to an audience, my answer to the question of who should create an Ethical Will is simple: "Look around the room. You have taken the time to come and hear about Ethical Wills. You should create one." I would say the same to you, the reader: you took the first step when you opened this book.

🎬3-4 Perhaps you've thought about those in your life, now passed, who have influenced you and wished there was a written record of their beliefs, life lessons and hopes. Many of us have known the blessing and burden of sorting and distributing the possessions of a friend or family member who is no longer able to do so, whether through infirmity or death. And just as many of us have hoped, down to the last box or drawer, to discover a letter or note, some evidence of a few moments spent putting affection or reflection on paper. So seldom is that wish fulfilled. So, like I said, "you should create one." You already know you have a message worth sharing. Make a pledge to *not* be a person who disappoints those left behind.

🎬3-5 Who creates an Ethical Will? You, once you realize that you have a message worth sharing. Take the time *now* to think about your message and then take the time to make a record of it.

🎬3-6 When you get to *Chapters Seven* through *Ten*, you'll find a variety of ways to express your Ethical Will. I'm sure at least one will appeal to you and your sense of style or creativity or simplicity. Or perhaps an idea will prompt you to create your own unique format, one I haven't even thought of.

Consider the task of writing your Ethical Will as a bucket list item with benefits. Writing an Ethical Will nurtures the writer as well as the reader. Identifying and naming the elements of this most personal of messages has a way of focusing the author on 🎬3-7 deeds not yet accomplished, ideals not yet met, aspirations newly discovered. It's not egotistical to offer up your personal philosophy on what makes life joyous or share your definition of man's duty to man or suggest the highest and best use of a Sunday afternoon. 🎬3-8 It's your footprint, your message, your personal

Notes to Self

message worth
sharing

mission statement. The people in your life who love you care what you think about life. There's no question that they would cherish a permanent record of what is the closest they will get to a distillation of your essence.

No, it's not unrealistic to put a message of such incredible consequence in just a few sentences or pages. It can be done, otherwise we'd be aiming for an Ethical Autobiography or an Ethical Epistle. Either one is an unrealistic goal for most of us. And, on the off chance you actually pulled it off, let's face it: few of your loved ones would willingly read the whole thing. ▄3-9 *In practice, your big message is your life, day in and day out—an Ethical Will is more like Cliff Notes®.* If you have beliefs and life lessons and hopes for the future—your tomorrow or your loved ones'—you should most definitely leave a written footprint and create your Ethical Will. But, as you are about to learn, an Ethical Will is not always about *you.*

▄3-10 Creating an Ethical Will for another: the Ethical Eulogy

If you are ever asked to write a eulogy for someone's funeral or memorial service, accept the request to enumerate someone's most unforgettable qualities as a great privilege. The Ethical Will is an excellent prototype for a eulogy. Given only a few minutes to speak, what better way to summarize the significance of a lifetime and bring comfort to those gathered than to focus on stories portraying the person's ▄3-11 core beliefs and values, the life lessons he or she shared by word and deed and the hopes for the future that were declared or demonstrated by that person?

An obituary tells about the person's birth, life and death. Well beyond those facts and statistics, an Ethical Eulogy tells what the person believed, knew and hoped for.

> ▄3-12 *My brother need not be idealized, or enlarged in death beyond what he was in life, to be remembered simply as a good and decent man, who saw wrong and tried to right it, saw suffering and tried to heal it, saw war and tried to stop it.*
>
> *Those of us who loved him and who take him to his rest today, pray that what he was to us and what he wished for others will some day come to pass for all the world.*
>
> *As he said many times, in many parts of this nation, to those he touched and who sought to touch him: "Some men see things as they are and say 'why?'. I dream things that never were and say 'why not?'."* [25]

🎬3-13 In 126 words, Edward Kennedy captured the essence of his fallen brother Robert Kennedy. The entire eulogy is considerably longer, but this is the part we remember; these are the core values displayed in this Ethical Eulogy and of the life it honored.

Please do not be daunted by the task of composing an Ethical Eulogy. 🎬3-14 Rather than focusing on the dates, times and places of a traditional eulogy—and the fear that someone or some event will be unknowingly omitted—focus on conveying a sense of the person's *spirit*. That is, in fact, much easier than trying to prioritize then recount the highlights and worldly accomplishments of an entire life in a few short minutes.

Not everyone is capable of producing prose as elegant as Edward Kennedy's and even fewer on short notice. 🎬3-15 But that's okay—the language of an Ethical Eulogy should reflect the nature of the person being eulogized. I was honored to write the tribute to my brother Wesley J. Kline. I guarantee he would have been horrified had I used flowery language or affected praise to recall examples of his kindness and loyalty. 🎬3-16

> *He loved that old-fashioned stuff like really knowing the people who live around him, family reunions and stopping in to visit the relatives that the rest of us only manage to see at weddings and funerals. Friendship with Wes was his lifelong commitment to be there when needed, touch base as often as possible and always accept others for what they are, not what they do or have.*
>
> *He was the one who always did what was needed, even before you knew you needed it. If you heard a snow plow in the driveway at 5:00 a.m. or a lawnmower in the yard, you knew it was Wes.*
>
> *In his absence, the best we can do is to follow the words Wes chose to be remembered by: "A life is not a brief candle—but a burning torch to be passed on."* [26] 🎬3-17

My brother Wes was as complex as any other person, but his beliefs and values were straightforward and clear-cut: 🎬3-18 *do the right thing and give back better than you get*. I tried to capture his simple philosophy in his eulogy by telling about the acts of kindness which he practiced on a daily basis and his attitude about the leukemia that took his life: a vivid reminder to do whatever it takes to get more of life and out of life. I would never claim that writing Wesley's eulogy was an easy task, but it went from impossible to doable when I realized that my biggest obstacle was choosing which examples of many best illustrated 🎬3-19 his *character* rather than his *achievements*.

🎬3-20 Writing the eulogy for my Uncle Tony Cebuhar (one of those relatives you're grateful to acquire by marriage) was a similar challenge. He was a delightful throw-back to simpler times when men came from low-down dirt poverty to stand out as decorated war heroes. He was married twice (*"It just never seemed to take..."*), buried all six of his siblings and lived out an unassuming and undemanding existence until his death at age ninety-three.

> *Tony was a great judge of character and perfectly captured the personality of those he met by assigning his own affectionate nickname to each. He was grateful for the smallest kindness shown to him and declared every holiday dinner, "the best time I've ever had."*
>
> *From Uncle Tony we learned an appreciation of life's tender mercies and the dignity of accepting life's not-so-tender misfortunes. A page out of history, Tony was a litany of life in America, and most of all, a gentle man.*[27]

Uncle Tony would also have rebuked any praise for his patriotism, his quirky and insightful sense of humor or even his youthful wine-making (back then, they called it *bootlegging*). But I like to think he approved of my tribute, shared with those who really knew him and attended his unpretentious funeral.

See if you can guess whose epitaph this is by the values and hopes it expresses:

> 🎬3-21 *She helped people. She laughed. She loved and is loved. She appreciated the world's natural beauty. She was curious and sought to learn who we are and what the universe is about. She relied on her own judgment and moral courage to do right. She cared about the suffering of her fellow man. She tried to protect our spaceship Earth. She taught her children to do the same.*

🎬3-22 These are the words inscribed on the grave marker for S. Christa McAuliffe, the high school teacher who died with six other crew members on January 28, 1986, in the Space Shuttle Challenger.[28] She is buried in Concord, New Hampshire. These simple descriptive sentences relate the most important lessons of her life and the hopes that live on after her passing. The author of her epitaph knew her well.

When it comes to eulogies, I'm an amateur. 🎬3-23 But here are some words of wisdom on the subject from someone who is most definitely not, speechwriter Peggy Noonan:

📽3-24 *[A eulogy] is the place to consider and highlight his obvious virtues—humor, warmth, steadfastness, insouciance, courage—and illustrate them if you can through anecdotes or pictures.*[29]

The tone of an Ethical Eulogy should reflect the person as well as the character traits that are listed. Note that the first "obvious virtue" Peggy Noonan mentioned was "humor." If you know the person well enough to be asked to write a eulogy, you know the role that wit played in his or her life. If there's no chuckling at my funeral, somebody missed the point. Specifically, Peggy-of-Irish-descent has this to say:

📽3-25 *A gentle humor is not inappropriate, and can lift people out of the moment; laughter leavens sorrow. But the comedy territory is obviously limited; as the Irish might say, you'll be wanting to save the belly laughs for the burial.*[30]

For those of us who are not professional speech writers and who may question our own qualifications to create a meaningful eulogy, Peggy assures us:

📽3-26 *...when you tell the truth clearly, without flourish, directly—and it is a truth worth hearing—chances are you will be very eloquent indeed.*[31]

📽3-27 While on the subject of Ethical Eulogies, I would be remiss if I failed to suggest that you write your eulogy as part of your end-of-life plans, modeled on the core elements of an Ethical Will. Putting your wishes for any funeral or memorial recognition in writing is the right thing to do. Think about it this way: is it really fair to ask your grief-stricken loved ones to plan one of the biggest events of your life (or afterlife) in a few short hours, all the while wondering what you would have wanted? Someone *will* read your Ethical Will at your service, so you might as well create a message appropriate for the occasion.

So pick out the clothes, the songs, the pallbearers, the resting place or cremation urn, the scripture or readings, whatever is appropriate to your beliefs, tastes and exit strategy. And remember, 📽3-28 1) it's your last chance to leave a nugget of wisdom and 2) it's for the living, not the recently deceased, so spare your loved ones the "just throw me in the ground" comment in lieu of specific instructions. Consider the perspective of your survivors by accepting the responsibility to make and communicate your plans. Making sure your loved ones know how you would like to be remembered is just plain good manners.

⬛3-29 Speaking in praise of the living: the Ethical Tribute

⬛3-30 Good news: a eulogy is "high praise" without requiring that the subject of the tribute must first be dead.[32] Although "eulogy" commonly refers to a tribute given at the funeral or memorial of a person who is no longer with us, it can also be written about and delivered to honor one who is still around to hear all the flattering comments. ⬛3-31 Anniversaries, milestone birthdays and retirement parties are all apt occasions to say nice things about someone. Wouldn't it be grand if the message of the typical roast or toast was meaningful and inspiring rather than just slightly humorous in an off-color, I-wrote-this-monologue-in-the-car sort of way?

Do more than merely recognize the circumstances that bring you together for a happy occasion. Rejoice in what makes the guest of honor special to those gathered in celebration: the essence of what he or she stands for.

⬛3-32 Making the past come alive: Ethical Genealogy

Earlier, I wrote about the correlation between a family tree and family values. How about making your family history come alive by telling the ethical history of your ancestors? ⬛3-33 It's one thing to tell where Grandmother was born, lived and died but so much more memorable to weave in the story of how her deep faith sustained her as she faced tragedy. ⬛3-34 Even just including favorite poems, prose or quotations can shine light on a person's essence, far beyond a mere sepia photo and historical dates. Keep in mind that no matter how distant in time and place, the leaves on your family tree were once real people with real solutions to life's quandaries.

⬛3-35 One of the methods for expressing an Ethical Will suggested in *Chapter Nine* is a family photo album, embellished with memories of the people pictured in it. ⬛3-36 The recollections of family members who knew an ancestor and what he or she stood for are sources of living history for those who come after. ⬛3-37 Another approach is to ask senior family members to share their remembrance of historical events that occurred during their lives. Then ask them to focus on how those events molded or sustained your family's values.

give thanks

⬛3-38 Letters of Gratitude

Although not technically an Ethical Tribute, this is a good place to put in a plug for Letters of Gratitude. They are the words you always mean to say but usually don't get around to saying.

⬛3-39 I wrote a letter to Ann Miller, my piano teacher until tenth grade (when I threw discipline aside for more social endeavors), to thank her for my love of music, which I continue to nurture (although admittedly not for at least thirty minutes every day). My first grade teacher, Ruby Dowell, was an exceptional example of dedication and love of children. We corresponded for many years after I graduated from her class in 1957.

I did not receive a response to either one, which is perfect, because the practice of sending thank you notes for thank you notes has gotten way out of hand. I'm glad I wrote to each of them what I had been meaning to say for many years: ⬛3-40 "You made a difference in my life. I learned from you and I appreciate the gifts you shared with me." Think about it. Then do it.

⬛3-41 *You have stories, wisdom, a message, a footprint. Make a record of what you stand for. Why? Because even though it's commendable and rewarding to create an Ethical Will, Ethical Tribute or Ethical Eulogy honoring another person, there is only one person who can really tell your story.* ⬛3-42 *There is only one person who is uniquely qualified to share what you believe, what you know and what you hope for. It's you.*

End of Chapter Three
⬛3-43

Review - Chapter Three

- The best reason to create an Ethical Will is to leave a record of what you stand for, to show appreciation for your life and your loved ones and as a permanent record of how you want to be remembered.

- The elements of an Ethical Will (beliefs and values, life lessons and hopes for the future) are an excellent outline for recalling the essence of one who has passed: an Ethical Eulogy.

- Focusing on the values, wisdom and hopes of someone can form the foundation of a meaningful Ethical Tribute, whenever a special occasion calls for words of praise and appreciation.

- A simple Letter of Gratitude is one way to make sure that those who have contributed to your ethical footprint know how much you appreciate their gifts of time and talents.

Ethical Eulogy

Ponder this...
Questions for discussion

1. What is it about the process or the end result of creating an Ethical Will that most appeals to you? _____

   _____

2. If you have ever written a Eulogy for someone, did you learn something new about the person in the process of writing about him or her? _____

   _____

3. Have you made detailed plans for your own memorial or funeral? Have you shared your plans with or made them available to loved ones? Please share any unusual ideas you have incorporated. Please share what it is like to picture yourself no longer here. _____

   _____

   _____

4. Have you written your eulogy? What is that experience like? _____

   _____

   _____

Now, let's exercise our creativity...
Chapter Three - Exercise 1

Imagine you are hosting a dinner to celebrate a milestone birthday for your dear, longtime friend. You will be giving a short speech, speaking about the very best parts of having this person in your life. Write about 100 words in tribute, focusing on the beliefs and values, life lessons and hopes of this person.

Example:

I first met Sheryl when I was a young attorney and she was a veteran real estate closer. Our friendship grew out of our mutual passion for being the very best at our jobs and being constantly disappointed in the work of others [audience laughter]. Sheryl taught me the real meaning of "friendship" and "family." She is the personification of "loyalty" and brings to every situation a sense of shared joy and unconditional love. I am grateful and proud to call her my friend.

Now, it's your turn (suggested: 10 minutes/100 words) _____

_____

_____

_____

_____

_____

_____

_____

_____
_____
_____
_____
_____
_____
_____
_____

Chapter Three - Exercise 2

Choose one of your relatives (living or passed on) and record your random thoughts about that person. Don't be concerned about form or eloquence. Just let your mind do the driving: focus on your memories of that person and, if possible, include some of the person's beliefs, wisdom or hopes in your reflections.

Example: *My Grandma Jones. Quiet strength. Liked to move. Patient. Kept her own counsel. Valued family—especially her grandchildren. Dignified. Devoted wife. Accepted her place in life. Doing crafts at her dining table. Walking "uptown" alongside her to buy groceries, greeting others with a "How do?"*

Now, it's your turn (suggested: 5 minutes) _____

little money

religious

generous

taste

loving

sense of humor

made us feel special

humble

Try not to become a man of success but a man of value.
Albert Einstein

ೞ **Notes to Self** ೲ

_____

_____

_____

_____

_____

_____

_____

_____

_____

_____

_____

_____

_____

_____

_____

_____

_____

_____

_____

_____

_____

_____

_____

_____

_____

_____

_____

_____

Share your knowledge.
It is a way to achieve immortality.
Dalai Lama
📽4-1

📽4-2 ℘ **Chapter Four** ℃
Your ever-widening circle of loved ones
(Who gets to share your Ethical Will?)

📽4-3 *Dear Luke,*

I wrote this book for your Grandpa. As I finish it, I realize how much it is also for you. Imagine when Grandpa was just about your age, he left high school to help win World War II. When the war was over, he came home and took on another mission: raising a family and educating his kids.

As you know, for most of his life, he worked two jobs and never complained. I have never seen him bitter or cynical about anything or anyone. To this day, Grandpa believes his glass is two-thirds full. Or, as he puts it "I am truly blessed." And so are you...

📽4-4 Written by Timothy John "Tim" Russert to his son Luke, these words are from the final pages of Tim's 2004 best-selling book, *Big Russ & Me.*[33] The book was Tim's tribute to his father, Timothy Joseph "Big Russ" Russert, crediting him for the foundation of Tim's core values and what Tim hoped would be his son Luke's as well.

In writing *Big Russ and Me*, Tim told the story of his father's lifetime of hard work, patriotism, commitment to values and family and of his influence on Tim's own life. I don't know if Tim Russert was familiar with the ancient tradition he was practicing. Did he know that his book was a contemporary example of an Ethical Tribute to Big Russ or that throughout the book—most especially in his letter to Luke—he was weaving his own Ethical Will, written just four years prior to his sudden death on June 13, 2008? Big Russ, Timothy Joseph Russert, passed away on September 24, 2009. *Big Russ and Me* serves as a well-deserved and comprehensive Ethical Eulogy for him as well.

📽4-5 The body of Tim Russert's work throughout his life and his role model as a son, husband, father, friend, mentor and journalist are the outline of his true footprint. But how precious for his immediate family, loved ones and countless admirers that he so succinctly spelled out what he stood for in this letter to Luke.

Notes to Self

_____

_____

_____

_____

_____

_____

_____

_____

_____

_____

_____

_____

_____

_____

_____

_____

_____

_____

_____

Tim Russert intended this Ethical Tribute and Ethical Will to be shared with the far-reaching audience of what he surely knew would be a best seller. Obviously, he anticipated that many unnamed others would be reading the personal mission statements woven throughout *Big Russ and Me*. He wanted to share with anyone and everyone the story of his father's legacy, its affirming influence on Tim's childhood and Tim's hopes for his son Luke. And rightfully so.

⚑4-6 One thing's for sure: by its very nature an Ethical Will is a message of your beliefs, lessons and hopes that *is meant to be shared*. It is not a question of whether there will be an audience for your Ethical Will, but simply how large. You may be thinking, "That's all well and good for someone with the fan base and talents of a Tim Russert, but seriously, who are the multitudes who will benefit from reading my Ethical Will?" Well, let's start with the obvious answer: those who know you and love you and who will appreciate being reminded—or perhaps surprised—to read the details of what you consider your ethical essence. ⚑4-7 The magnitude of your intended audience depends on your age, your family structure, the vastness of your circle of friends, maybe even an extended base of admirers and, of course, the motivation for creating and sharing your message. The size of the audience may also be affected by the medium you choose to express your Ethical Will. Personal letters will naturally be directed solely to the addressee while an embellished family photo album can be scanned and shared with every member of your clan. In the next chapter, I talk about *when* to share your Ethical Will and that decision may also influence with whom you share it.

Let's categorize potential levels of exposure, and you can choose which one is most appropriate for you. When we get down to the nitty gritty of creating your Ethical Will in *Chapter Eleven*, you'll see that one of the first and most important questions to ask yourself is ⚑4-8 *"Who will be sharing my Ethical Will?"* so it's best to start thinking about that now.

⚑4-9 **Level I sharing.** This is your immediate family, your children and/or grandchildren and closest friends. In reality, it may be just one or a few from each group, the ones you are closest to or who you believe will most appreciate your message.

⚑4-10 **Level II sharing.** In addition to those in Level I, perhaps you will want to share your Ethical Will with your extended family (your twigs and leaves) or any organizations you belong to that exemplify your beliefs. If you are using your Ethical Will to practice Footprint Philanthropy™, consider sharing your Ethical Will with your legal or financial advisors and then with the charities' representatives, so they will better understand why they were chosen and your expectations for the use of your gifts. The same goes for anyone you have chosen to act as trustee for the distribution of your assets or the successive guardian of your dependents. And if you are leaving heirlooms to family members or loved ones in your Will, sharing your Ethical Will can provide deeper meaning to the treasures you leave and why each recipient was chosen.

4-11 **Level III sharing.** This is for the serious communicator who sees the potential for a wider audience, perhaps including strangers. If you are a blogger or use one of the many social media sources, e.g. Facebook or LinkedIn, consider sharing your Ethical Will online. A mass e-mail quickly delivers your thoughts to everyone in your address book. If you believe your message will resonate with others who share your belief system, think about having it posted on the website of your church or fraternal organization. 4-12 How about leaving a copy to be forwarded to your classmates upon your death (better yet: *before* your death!) to be shared at the next reunion. And an Ethical Will can be an effective foundation of your obituary. Consider including it in your final wishes for funeral or memorial plans (there's a better than good chance that someone will read it at your service whether or not you suggest it). Or, write a book!

4-13 When I teach about Ethical Wills, I usually include the most recent version of my Ethical Will (it is a constantly evolving work-in-progress) in slideshow format. I always smile as I observe the giggles and aahs elicited by the photos and quotations I have included. 4-14 Most importantly, I know the class members are beginning to 1) realize how well one can come to know a person by watching a mere three minute slideshow; 2) appreciate how moving it can be to glimpse into another person's value system, and 3) believe that they, too, can create an Ethical Will that reflects a personal mission statement. 4-15 *"The media becomes the message."* [34]

4-16 *Traditions are family practices that are handed down from one generation to the next. They may revolve around holidays, gathering places, religion, heirlooms or even food. Think about starting a tradition in your family that comes from creating and sharing a meaningful written message of your beliefs and values, life lessons and hopes for the future. And then perhaps widen your "family" circle.*

End of Chapter Four
and
Workshop and Slideshow Session I
4-17

Review - Chapter Four

- An Ethical Will is the legacy of what you stand for and it is meant to be shared.
- Who you share your Ethical Will with is a personal decision. The audience can be as small as your immediate circle of friends and family, or as big as the internet audience for your Facebook page.

Ponder this...
Questions for discussion

1. How do you feel about sharing your Ethical Will with anyone outside your immediate family? _____
   _____

2. Share your thoughts on the advantages and disadvantages of "going public" with an Ethical Will. _____
   _____

3. Will the content or format of your Ethical Will be affected by how many or with whom you plan to share the message? _____
   _____

4. Is there someone you wish had created an Ethical Will and shared it with you? Why?
   _____
   _____

5. If someone has shared his or her Ethical Will with you, were you surprised to be included in that audience? _____
   _____

Now, let's exercise our creativity...
Chapter Four - Exercise 1

Think about the people with whom you plan to share your Ethical Will. Then write three sentences as a "Prelude" to your Ethical Will, telling them why you decided to create an Ethical Will and what you hope they will gain from hearing it.

Example:

I plan to share my Ethical Will with my family.

"If you are surprised to share my Ethical Will, don't be. You are my family and are the people in my life who have most made me feel loved and part of a larger world and plan. I hope the thoughts contained in my Ethical Will somehow make your own journey through life a little easier."

Now, it's your turn (suggested: 10 minutes/3 sentences) _____

_____

_____

_____

_____

_____

Chapter Four - Exercise 2

Revisit the mental list you just made of the people with whom you will share your Ethical Will. Now, choose three of them and address a sentence to each: tell what values each person has that made him or her such a special part of your life—so exceptional that they will be sharing your Ethical Will. It will be like a mini-Ethical Tribute to that person.

Example:

Katie: You are determined and headstrong—that and your sense of humor and compassion will serve you well through life.

Jack: There is a special light shining behind that quick wit and cockeyed optimism—I hope it never dims.

Phyllis: Your model as a friend and sister and mother has taught me about patience and what it really means to be a family.

Now, it's your turn (suggested: 10 minutes/3 sentences) _____

Life is a series of lessons
Which must be lived to be understood.
Thomas Carlyle

ೲ **Notes to Self** ೲ

🎬5-1 <u>WORKSHOP and SLIDESHOW SESSION II</u>

Life really does begin at forty.
Up until then, you are just doing research.
Carl Jung
🎬5-2

🎬5-3 ഇ Chapter Five രു
If the spirit moves you, it's time
(When to create an Ethical Will)

🎬5-4
2,428,272,000 seconds
40,471,200 minutes
674,520 hours
28,105 days
77 years

That's life expectancy in the United States.

It sounds like a long time unless you've been alive for at least half of it. You know it really isn't when you find yourself thinking: "If the next 20 years go as fast as the last 20 years did, I'll be (fill-in-the-blank with "60", "70", "80", "dead") before I know it." Personally, I like Bernard Baruch's quotation: 🎬5-5 *"To me, old age is always 15 years older than I am."* At any rate, the older you get, the faster the years go by. It must be that space/time continuum thing.

🎬5-6 Clearly, any one of life's transitions (birth, death, a first home, a wedding, an anniversary, a divorce, separation, empty-nesting, moving, a serious illness, retirement) contains the potential for self-reflection: looking back and looking forward. Seeing members of your extended family at a 🎬5-7 wedding puts a face on the passage of time, a funeral is a dramatic reminder of the fragility of life, a milestone anniversary makes you think of the lessons only marriage can teach, and the birth of a grandchild is a sweet illustration of the circle of life. Something starts you thinking, and if that thinking prompts you to put thoughts on paper and share what you believe, what you know and what you hope for, then all the better. You may be jarred into putting your message into words by one of life's major transitions or because you finally made it a priority and found the time. 🎬5-8 The late Rabbi Richard J. Israel wrote four very special letters to his daughter: on the day of her birth, when she left home for college, on the eve of

Notes to Self
_____
_____
_____
_____
_____
_____
_____
_____
_____
_____
_____
_____
_____
_____
_____
_____
_____
_____

her marriage and upon the birth of her first child, his grandchild.[35] Good luck trying to beat that.

5-9 True, there are decisive events that prompt an Ethical Will on a time-sensitive basis. If you are using your Ethical Will to guide your end-of-life health care and estate planning and to enlighten family members about your decisions, you will need to craft your ethical message ahead of the legal documents. 5-10 Young or not so young, if you are facing a career or job change, an Ethical Will that includes your professional values, lessons and hopes can be key in guiding your decision-making process. If you are writing the Ethical Eulogy for another who has recently passed, time is definitely of the essence. If you receive a bad prognosis and know for a fact that your time is limited, well, you should probably make your Ethical Will a more urgent priority. If your youngest child is getting married, you not only have wisdom to share, you are about to become an empty-nester. Perfect timing for an Ethical Will.

5-11 Please do not get tangled up in the assumption that you need some minimum number of years before your wisdom has sufficiently ripened. I can only guess that Rabbi Israel, if like most others, gained insight over the years and that his last letter probably well outshined his first for finesse and wisdom. But no passage of time or experience can replace the unmatched expert reflections contained in the very first letter: a young father expressing his pride and dreams upon the birth of his daughter.[36]

5-12 I referenced my own work-in-progress Ethical Will. Its evolving state of completion is due partly to my desire to practice new media, partly to my obsessive belief that the best version is always the next version and partly to the constant evolution of the lessons I want to share. 5-13 It is, after all, my essence we're talking about here. Like yours, it is ever-changing and—hopefully—ever-enriching.

You can do the same. The installments of your serial Ethical Will can reflect the chapters of your life. 5-14 It can be a series of letters to loved ones, written each New Year's Day. It can be a brief note written every year to accompany a child's class picture. It can be a special message given to children or grandchildren as they reach milestones in their own lives: graduation, marriage, a home, a child.

I hope as you approach *Chapters Seven* through *Ten* you begin to appreciate that there is very little about Ethical Wills that is universal. 5-15 The core elements of values, lessons and hope are defining, but beyond that, each Ethical Will is as unique as each creator. Every person has a distinctive Ethical Will within, just waiting for inspiration, timing and method to come together.

🎬5-16 *Whether you are motivated by the birth of a child, grandchild, retirement or a life-threatening prognosis is of no matter; the time to create an Ethical Will is when plan and opportunity meet. You are formulating your plan by reading this book.* 🎬5-17 *Put your strategy into motion and take this opportunity to start writing your Ethical Will soon after you finish reading this book—very soon after.*

End of Chapter Five
🎬5-18

Review - Chapter Five

- Any one of life's transitions contains the potential for self-reflection and can trigger the creation of an Ethical Will.
- Birth, death, a first home, a wedding, an anniversary, separation, empty-nesting, moving, a serious illness, retirement, or the approaching end of life are milestones that may prompt you to make a permanent record of your beliefs and values, life lessons and hopes for the future.
- The time to create your Ethical Will is when plan and opportunity meet.

Ponder this...
Questions for discussion

1. What milestone in your life, if any, prompted you to think about creating and sharing your Ethical Will? _____ _____

2. Can you think of an unusual life event or transition that would be a fitting time to reflect and create an Ethical Will that you would not normally think of? How about the death of a pet? Or a trusted neighbor moving away? _____ _____

3. Looking back, can you think of a life transition, event or crisis that would have been more easily experienced if you had used an Ethical Will to self-reflect or to sort out your feelings?_____ _____

4. If you consider creating a serial Ethical Will (one that you add to as time goes by), what annual event would be likely to prompt you to continue the practice? New Year's? Thanksgiving? Your birthday? Ground Hog Day? _____ _____

5. How old does someone need to be to have "wisdom" worth sharing? _____

_____

_____

_____

Now, let's exercise our creativity...
Chapter Five - Exercise 1

Create an Ethical Will time capsule of your life. It will contain events that have been the most influential in forming your core values. Unfortunately, the capsule only has room for <u>two</u> items/events in it, so choose wisely. Then tell why each event earned a place in the time capsule.

Example:

1. *I was twenty-eight years old when my first husband, Roy Z. Fort, died suddenly. Since that day I have realized that I am not immortal and that I will someday leave this earth for the next place in my journey. That acknowledgement makes me more appreciative of the brevity of life and the importance of every day and all that it contains.*

2. *I knew from the moment I saw my second husband, John (we were reunited at our 20-year high school reunion) that we would be married. Finding John again and sharing my life with him makes me understand that there is a "plan" and that I need to be intent on paying attention to the signs that life brings my way.*

Now, it's your turn (suggested: 10 minutes) _____

_____

_____

_____

_____

_____

_____

_____

_____

_____

_____

_____

_____

_____

_____

_____

_____

_____

_____

Chapter Five - Exercise 2

What do you know now that you didn't know then? Think of a milestone in your own life—it can be a sad event or the happiest day of your life. Focus on what you learned from that transition in your life. What was different about you after that event, as compared to before? Think in terms of your value system and any life lessons learned.

Example:

I went to law school after the death of my first husband. In the middle of the first semester, I just didn't think I had it in me to finish. I went to my parents and vented, with lots of tears. My father suggested that I try to just make it to the end of the semester. That way, if I ever decided to return, I would have those core courses completed—and I would not have wasted the tuition. My father died one year later but his advice to focus on "one moment at a time" is what got me through that semester and ultimately to my law degree three years later. I have applied that wisdom to many situations since: when I thought I just couldn't make it to the end, my goal became to make it through now.

It's your turn (suggested: 10 minutes) _____

_____

_____

_____

_____

_____

_____

_____

_____

_____

_____

_____

_____

_____

_____

_____

_____

_____

_____

_____

_____

_____

_____

A story should have a beginning, a middle, and an end...
but not necessarily in that order.
Jean Luc Goddard

ℰℴ Notes to Self ℭ℞

"What wisdom would we impart to the world
if we knew it was our last chance?
Randy Pausch
🎬6-1

🎬6-2 ℘ Chapter Six ℘
You'll know when the time is right
(When to share an Ethical Will)

🎬6-3 Carnegie Mellon, the Pittsburgh university of 10,000 students, hosts an ongoing series of presentations in which faculty members speak, sharing "their reflections on their journeys—the everyday actions, decisions, challenges and joys that make a life."[37] Invited instructors are asked to focus on what matters from the imagined perspective of a person facing death and delivering his or her last campus lecture. Sometime prior to September 2007, Carnegie Mellon made the decision to change the name of the series from *The Last Lecture* to *Journeys*.[38] We now know that attempting to retire the original title was premature.

🎬6-4 In September of 2006, Randy Pausch, a 46-year-old professor of computer science at Carnegie Mellon University, had just been diagnosed with pancreatic cancer. He underwent a regimen of aggressive treatments, but a year later, about the same time his turn came to participate in *Journeys*, he received news that his latest and last available treatment had failed and that his prognosis was terminal, his remaining life measured in months. A husband and father of three, Randy's decision to proceed with *Journeys* is best explained in his own words: "Many people might expect the talk to be about dying. But it had to be about *living*."[39]

🎬6-5 Randy Pausch delivered his last lecture, "Really Achieving Your Childhood Dreams," to an audience of 400 at Carnegie Mellon on September 18, 2007. It is touching, generous, telling, funny, sad and, most of all, inspiring. One is mesmerized, watching as the vibrant-appearing young man thanks all the people in his life who gave him a hand up, all the while knowing that he is not going to live much longer.

Randy asked that the lecture be videotaped. That DVD is surely a continuing source of inspiration for the 400 people gathered that day and certainly an irreplaceable treasure of his beliefs and values, life lessons and hopes for his three young children. Achieving either one of those goals would have been incredible and extraordinary. Then along came Oprah. Someone told her about the last lecture given by Professor Randy Pausch,

Notes to Self

and she told 7.4 million of her closest friends, and then Randy Pausch's last lecture took on a life of its own. Not sharing his Ethical Will with a worldwide audience was no longer an option for Randy Pausch.

Randy Pausch's last lecture was uploaded onto YouTube, the internet place-to-be for videos, and, as of this writing, has been viewed more than eleven million times. ▰6-6 The book, *The Last Lecture*, naturally followed the video. In it, Randy and co-author Jeffrey Zaslow had the opportunity to expand Randy's personal philosophy well beyond the restrictions of a one hour and sixteen minute speech. *The Last Lecture* is a 206-page Ethical Will and, as Ethical Wills go, it's as good as it gets.[40] Randy Pausch was dying and he acknowledged it, quoting his father: "...my dad always taught me that when there's an elephant in the room, introduce it," which makes Randy's approach to his death also one of the most mindful ever observed.[41]

Randy said he was using his *Journeys* speech "to really think about what matters most to me, to cement how people will remember me, and to do whatever good I can on the way out." He also thought the presentation would help his wife Jai supply a tangible answer to his children's future questions: "Who was my dad? What was he like?"[42] He answered those questions, *and* he provided a role model for a life well-lived and for talking about a life well-lived for the millions of readers of his book and the viewers of his DVD. The message of his life will be shared with his most important audience, his three children, as time goes by. *The Last Lecture* illustrates the sometimes obvious choice of *when* to share your Ethical Will: when circumstances dictate.

Sometimes the *when* of sharing wisdom is by happenstance. In ▰6-7 *Wisdom of Our Fathers,* Tim Russert's follow up to *Big Russ and Me*, he shared a story submitted by Stuart Frankel of New York City. When Stuart was eleven, he and his father, Adrian Frankel, lingered in front of a funeral parlor, observing as a crowd entered, then departed twenty minutes later. When questioned by young Stuart, his father explained the importance of that moment to his eleven-year-old son, availing himself of a teachable moment:

> *Because I hope you will live a long and productive life, that you will be aware of your surroundings, that you will stay out of trouble, and that you will be thoughtful and cautious. And above all, that you will always know in the back of your mind that someday your entire life will be summed up in twenty minutes.[43]*

Stuart Frankel wrote to Tim Russert in 2004 to share this unforgettable moment that had stayed with him for more than 53 years. ▰6-8 Let's say you have made the decision to create your Ethical Will with clear instructions that it is to be shared with your loved ones once you have passed away. But, wait a minute! As you're writing about some valuable life lessons learned in your 40s, you suddenly realize that your son is in his 40s! Might there be some benefit to him if you imparted your wisdom right now and didn't make him wait until you're dead and he's in his 60s? I think so, too.

If you already know that you want your Ethical Will to be a part of your memorial, so be it. That does not mean, however, that you cannot also share its contents with close family members and loved ones prior to that time. It just means that even more people will hear it later.

☙6-9 Some timing is self-evident. For instance, making decisions and preparing the necessary documentation is the *first* step in taking responsibility for planning how you want to be treated at the end of your life. No less important than preparing your end-of-life plan is communicating your wishes to your loved ones and empowering them to act on your behalf if that becomes necessary. Not doing so is putting your loved ones in the unenviable position of guessing what you would want them to do. Proxy decision makers cannot advocate unknown instructions.

The two documents (an advance directive can be a combination form, subject to your state's law) that you need for health care decision-making are the following: ☙6-10

- **Living Will**: your instructions for care at the end of life if you have a terminal or irreversible condition, assuming you are not able to manage your care at that time.
- **Durable Power of Attorney for Health Care**: the appointment of your substitute decision-makers, a proxy and a backup proxy, to speak for you and to make sure your wishes are respected in any health care situation in which you are not able to manage your care.

☙6-11 An effective Living Will suggests situations that may occur and specifies your instructions in each event.[44] However, there are end-of-life situations that cannot be anticipated. In that event, the moral compass your loved ones will need is provided by knowing your general views on life, how you measure quality vs. quantity and when you want life-prolonging measures to be discontinued. If you are using an Ethical Will to guide your end-of-life planning, the time to share it with your health care proxies and other close loved ones is as soon as you have completed all your legal and legacy documents.

☙6-12 Making a job or career change is a transition that affects everyone in your circle of life. If you have created your Ethical Will as part of your decision-making process, sharing its contents will enlighten your loved ones on the rationale for your professional goals and for your career choice.

☙6-13 If you are writing your Ethical Will or an Ethical Tribute to another, motivated by a special occasion (☙6-14 a wedding, a baptism, the birth of a child or grandchild, a milestone birthday, a family or class reunion, an anniversary, a career change, retirement), the timing is obvious. And don't throw away your preparatory notes! They have a special place among your treasures or those of the honored person.

&6-15 Fiction writers often say, when asked how a story line came to be, that the characters acted out the story on their own; the yarn spun itself once the author invited the characters in. And so it can be with your Ethical Will: permit your story, the creation of your Ethical Will, to guide the choice of when to share as well as who your audience will be.

&6-16 Every writer of every Ethical Will has a different story to tell, and a unique audience with whom to share that message. If you're committed to crafting a message of what you believe, what you know and what you hope for, the question of "when to share" somehow answers itself. Once created, an Ethical Will needs, even demands, to be shared. &6-17 It doesn't require life-altering circumstances or even a special occasion. It just needs an audience.

End of Chapter Six
&6-18

Review - Chapter Six

- *When* you share your Ethical Will is a personal decision, based on who your audience may be, the circumstances of creating it and—most importantly—the nature of your message.

- Although it is sometimes beyond our control, if you do have input on when to share your Ethical Will, consider those who could use your shared wisdom as soon as possible.

- Creating your Ethical Will can be a well-timed first step in preparing some legal documents that you should also have: a Living Will that specifies your wishes for care at the end of your life or if your condition is irreversible and a Durable Power of Attorney for Health Care that delegates your health care decision-making to a proxy and a backup proxy.

Ponder this...
Questions for discussion

1. Have you thought about when you want to share your own Ethical Will? If so, when and why? _____

_____

2. What are the advantages, if any, of sharing your Ethical Will with loved ones while you are still around, rather than at your memorial or funeral? _____

_____

_____

3. Have you ever had the opportunity to reveal an Ethical Will-type writing at the memorial or funeral of a loved one? If so, please share what that experience meant to you. _____

_____

_____

4. What about leaving instructions to share your Ethical Will after you are gone? Where is a good place to store your instructions and Ethical Will in the meantime? _____

_____

_____

_____

5. Have you ever received someone else's ethical message and wished you had gotten it earlier (either while the person was still living or at an earlier stage of your own life)?

_____

_____

_____

Now, let's exercise our creativity...
Chapter Six - Exercise 1

Can you think of a pearl of wisdom that someone shared with you when you were younger? Write about that person and the life lesson they shared with you—focus on why it stuck with you all these years.

Example:

The man who once most wisely said,
"Be sure you're right, then go ahead,"
Might well have added this, to wit:
"Be sure you're wrong before you quit."

This nugget came from my Grandmother Elizabeth (Hardie) Jones—she had clipped it from a church bulletin and mailed it to me. I was probably 7 or 8 years old at the time. Because she was a woman of few words, it is precious to me that she expressed this sentiment through a poem. It has stayed with me because it is among very few recorded thoughts from my Grandmother Jones and because its message is so very true—as I have learned many times over.

Now, it's your turn (suggested: 10 minutes) _____

_____

_____

_____

_____

_____

_____

_____

_____

_____

_____

Chapter Six - Exercise 2

Think of a person no longer in your life whose opinion you valued. Pose a question you wish you had asked and imagine the answer, based on what you remember about his or her beliefs and values.

Example:

I wish I had asked my Uncle Bill if he had any regrets about his professional career: Did he wish he had been more of an entrepreneur and less of a corporate leader?

He was very pragmatic. I think he would say that he did what he did because that is where fate took him. He also respected the role of big business in keeping our economy running smoothly and providing infrastructure, so I believe he would say that he used his entrepreneurial talents to lead the railroad company to its success. He would also tell me that he considered his leadership in political and civic matters to be important elements of his ethical footprint.

Now, it's your turn (suggested: 10 minutes) _____

_____

_____

_____

_____

_____

_____

_____

_____

_____

_____

_____

_____

_____

_____

_____

🎬II-1 Part II.
From papyrus to the big screen: expressing your Ethical Will

🎬II-2 It is no accident that the subtitle of this book is _Creating_ an Ethical Will—not _Writing_ an _Ethical Will._ You are about to see that there are many possible ways to express your Ethical Will. Some do not involve any writing and none require any exceptional writing skills. 🎬II-3 Creating a meaningful Ethical Will is about identifying your unique message, speaking from your heart, and finding the most effective way to communicate your Ethical Will. So stop saying, _"But I'm no writer."_

In the next three chapters, I share ideas for expressing an Ethical Will, assist in choosing the best format and suggest methods to guide your message and prompts to get you started. New ways to craft an Ethical Will come into my view every day, and they will for you as well, once you learn to recognize them.

🎬II-4 Keep in mind that the core elements of any Ethical Will are one's 1) beliefs and values, 2) life lessons learned, and 3) hopes for the future. It's a worthy goal to be all-inclusive, but please allow that not every Ethical Will contains all three essentials in an orderly, identifiable manner. If it reveals some of a person's wisdom, message, or footprint, it qualifies. If it articulates what works in life, what should be avoided or what one should strive for, it qualifies. If, after reading or viewing it, you sense what someone stands for, and you leave with a nugget you can use going forward, it qualifies.

🎬II-5 So open your mind to the nearly limitless options for crafting an Ethical Will. (Visit the Endnotes for legible copy of the poetry and prose contained in _Part II_.) 🎬II-6 Maybe one will strike your fancy or perhaps you will envision a combination of several to embrace your personal message to loved ones. The important thing is that you think beyond the ancient example of a beautifully scripted letter if that's just not your style.

This _Part, Chapters Seven_ through _Ten_, is filled with examples of Ethical Wills. It shows the variety of media that may be used to express your Ethical Will, an Ethical Eulogy or an Ethical Tribute. They range from the simple to the complex, from time-honored traditional to high-tech contemporary. For each example presented in these chapters, stop and reflect on whether it is one that works for you and consider the following: 🎬II-7

- _Is it a medium that I am willing to use and that allows me to express the message of my Ethical Will?_
- _Will it communicate my message to those with whom I plan to share my Ethical Will?_
- _Most importantly, is it me? Does the style of this Ethical Will feel right?_

Every production of an artist should be
the expression of an adventure of his soul.
W. Somerset Maugham

℘ **Notes to Self** ℜ

*The secret to creativity
is knowing how to hide your sources.*
Albert Einstein
🎬 7-1

🎬 7-2 ℘ Chapter Seven ℀
Using the words of others

Notes to Self

🎬 7-3 *Originality* should not be confused with *creativity*. *Originality* is "the quality of newness that exists in something not done before or not derived from anything else." Creativity means "the ability to think creatively and depart from traditional or previous forms."[45] So it is clear that one can demonstrate great creativity in crafting something—say, for instance, an Ethical Will—without being the originator of its components. That's where the creative art of 🎬 7-4 *using the words of others* comes in.

🎬 7-5 ℘ Quotations ℀

I wish I'd said this, but the Scottish novelist Anna Masterton Buchan (pen name: O. Douglas) beat me to it: 🎬 7-6 *"I know heaps of quotations, so I can always make quite a fair show of knowledge."* I could not agree more. 🎬 7-7 If God had meant for me to think of all the really great stuff, he would not have given me the wisdom of Ralph Waldo Emerson, David Thoreau, Will Rogers, Mark Twain, and many others.

If there are one or more quotations that resonate with the key messages of your Ethical Will, it would be downright silly to try to come up with something original. There are three types of quotations for use in an Ethical Will, Ethical Tribute or Ethical Eulogy:

🎬 7-8 1) *First person quotations:* Quotations attributed directly to the subject of the Ethical Will. I know people who say quotable things on a daily basis. I'm not entirely convinced that all—or any—of them would be appropriate to include in an Ethical Will or prose of any nature, but it's definitely original material and sometimes even worth repeating;

🎬 7-9 2) *Re-quotes:* Quotations or writings that, although written by another person, were favorites of the subject or were once re-quoted by the subject. Musings or quotations that he or she admired and that reflect his or her philosophy, humor or outlook on life are especially meaningful and

◉7-10 3) *Things I wish I'd said:* Quotations that are fitting to the subject of the Ethical Will or directly reflect something you learned from knowing the person. It may be a sentence, an essay or a paragraph that makes you think of the one you are reflecting on, as if written just for or about that person.

Here are examples of quotations that could be used in my Ethical Will:

◉7-11 1) *First person quotation:* To describe my family members, I coined the phrase *"It is better to be a Kline than to be married to a Kline."* If you doubt that, just ask one of the in-laws.

◉7-12 2) *Re-quote:* Here is one of my favorite quotations; so dear to me that it is inscribed on the wall of our living room: *"A little song, a little dance, a little seltzer down the pants."* [46]

◉7-13 3) *Things I wish I'd said:* I recently found this quotation from Harold V. Melchert and think it makes a lovely statement about life, or at least one I aspire to: *"Live your life each day as you would climb a mountain: an occasional glance toward the summit keeps the goal in mind, but many beautiful scenes are to be observed from each new vantage point."* Mindfulness.

◉7-14 Back in *Chapter Four*, I displayed a small part of the inspiration that Tim Russert left in the letter he wrote to his son Luke. How interesting that in this letter he went on to quote a 15-word commencement speech he had once heard and admired: *"The best exercise of the human heart is reaching down and pulling someone else up."* [47] If I'm not mistaken, Tim Russert is referring to a speech delivered by ◉7-15 Jon Huntsman, corporate renaissance man extraordinaire and author of *Winners Never Cheat.* [48] And Jon Huntsman got it from a plaque that hangs behind his desk, an inspiring nugget by John Andrew Holmes, Jr. Tim Russert's book is the mother lode of Ethical Will examples: a *book-length Ethical Will* containing a *personal letter Ethical Will* which cites the *one-liner Ethical Will* as an Ethical commencement speech, which was a *re-quote* courtesy of John Andrew Holmes, Jr. Quite a legacy.

So, as you consider using quotations as all or part of an Ethical Will, remember that you are not limited to just one of these categories. ◉7-16 You can mix and match *first person*, *re-quotes* and *things I wish I'd said* to best express the message of your Ethical Will or an Ethical Eulogy or Ethical Tribute to another. And always, always credit the author of any material you use.

◉7-17 ℘ **One-liners** ☙

Can the philosophy of a life be expressed in just one sentence? You be the judge.

📽7-18
So many of our dreams at first seem impossible,
Then they seem improbable,
And then, when we summon the will,
They soon become inevitable.

📽7-19 Those were the words of someone who knew a lot about challenging inevitability and overcoming improbabilities. They were spoken by Christopher Reeve—aka Superman—who made his indelible mark on this world in spite of the tragic spinal cord injury that cost him his mobility and ultimately his life. I would argue that this sentence could describe Christopher Reeve's philosophy of life, his essence.

Consider the immense wisdom embodied by these few words from President Abraham Lincoln: 📽7-20

And, in the end, it is not the years in your life that count;
it is the life in your years.

He expressed a whole lot in just 30 words. So did Robert Louis Stevenson, in 14 words: 📽7-21

There is no duty we so much underrate
as the duty of being happy.

And Dr. Seuss (Theodor Seuss Geisel), in 21 words: 📽7-22

Be who you are and say what you feel because those
who mind don't matter and those who matter don't mind.

William Shakespeare, who gave us so many words, also gave us this very brief bit of wisdom: 📽7-23

Love all, trust a few, do wrong to none.

Albert Einstein's words, however, are my favorite: 📽7-24

If A is a success in life, then A equals x plus y plus z.
Work is x; y is play; and z is keeping your mouth shut.

Actually, one-liner Ethical Wills have been around for a very long time. 📽7-25 The Bible refers to one scribed on the grave of Abel, son of Adam: *"Here was shed the blood of the righteous Abel"* and it doesn't get much earlier than that. These one-liners are commonly known as epitaphs. Some were meant to discourage grave robbers, some as a final "ah ha!"[49] and others were intended to distill the meaning of a life into a few, short words:

7-26   *Liberty, humanity, justice, equality*
Susan Brownell Anthony
February 15, 1820 – March 13, 1906

Or this one at the burial site of The Duke: 7-27

Tomorrow is the most important thing in life,
Comes into us at midnight very clean,
It's perfect when it arrives and it puts itself in our hands,
It hopes we've learned something from yesterday.
John Wayne
May 26, 1907 – June 11, 1979

Actually, John Wayne wanted his epitaph to read: "Feo, Fuerte y Formal," which means "He was ugly, strong and had dignity" but his final wishes were ignored, which is probably just as well.[50]

So yes, one line can do the job.

Is there a quotation that speaks to you, a short phrase that seems to epitomize all that you stand for? Don't you remember? You wrote it down somewhere when you first heard it, it sounded so true, so memorable.   7-28 If not, visit one or more of the countless quotation sites on the internet to browse and find the pithy expression that says it all.[51]

Here are two examples of an   7-29 *embellished quotation*, a one-liner with a picture. Together they tell a story. These messages from my own PowerPoint Ethical Will are simple. The first slide shows that one of the greatest joys of my life is being able to share it with my husband and the little people dear to us. As for the second slide, I couldn't come up with this thought if I spent my whole life trying, so thank you, George Elliott. And, yes, that's really me.[52]

7-30

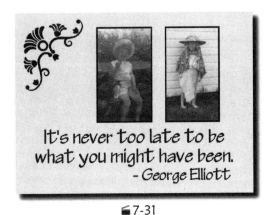

It's never too late to be
what you might have been.
- George Elliott

7-31

7-32 My friend Mary Kay Shanley is a best-selling author and gifted teacher of creative and memoir writing. Together we composed her Ethical Will slideshow: photos and quotations from Mary Kay and computer know-how from me. Here are two slides from her Ethical Will featuring her mother Irene Geishecker Shanley and her father George Thomas Shanley. Although these are from Mary Kay's Ethical Will, she decided to make her mother's and father's legacies part of her message.

Either you are interesting
at any age or you are not.
- Katherine Hepburn

7-33

Safe, for a child,
is her father's hand,
holding her tight.
- Marion C. Garretty

7-34

Mary Kay chose photos and quotations that perfectly express her affection for her parents, speak to the character of each and pass on Mary Kay's own views as an echo of her parents'.[53]

☙7-35 ℘ Thumbnail essays ℘

☙7-36 Samuel Langhorne Clemens (aka Mark Twain) was licensed as a steamboat pilot in 1859 at the age of 24. Living on the Mississippi until the Civil War put a stop to paddle wheeler activity, Twain acquired his pen name and the perspective he displayed in this nugget of wisdom:[54]

> *Twenty years from now you will be more disappointed by the things you didn't do than by the ones you did do. So throw off the bowlines. Sail away from the safe harbor. Catch the trade winds in your sails. Explore. Dream. Discover.*

It's brief, to the point, succinct but sufficient. Much like this astute advice from Ralph Waldo Emerson: ☙7-37

> *To laugh often and much; to win the respect of intelligent people and the affection of children; to earn the appreciation of honest critics and to endure the betrayal of false friends. To appreciate beauty; to find the best in others; to leave the world a bit better whether by a healthy child, a garden patch, or a redeemed social condition; to know that even one life has breathed easier because you have lived. This is to have succeeded.*[55]

☙7-38 The very livelihoods of Twain and Emerson were as dependent on the volume as on the quality of their writing. It is a lesson in humility to witness their ability to leave words on the cutting room floor, exposing the simple core message. It shows that not only *can* you create an Ethical Will using very few words—your own or those of another—but that perhaps you *should*. Sometimes the less you say, the more you say. Make that: sometimes less is more.

From Robert Louis Stevenson: ☙7-39

> *Give us grace and strength to forbear and to persevere. Give us courage and gaiety and the quiet mind. Spare to us our friends and soften to us our enemies. Give us the strength to encounter that which is to come, that we may be brave in peril, constant in tribulation, temperate in wrath and in all changes of fortune, and down to the gates of death, loyal and loving to one another.*

And also from Stevenson:

> *It is not likely that posterity will fall in love with us, but not impossible that it may respect or sympathize; so a man would rather leave behind him the portrait of his spirit than a portrait of his face.*

This short list of dos and don'ts came from the Buddha: ▰7-40

> *Do not believe in anything simply because you have heard it. Do not believe in anything simply because it is spoken and rumored by many. Do not believe in anything simply because it is found written in your religious books. Do not believe in anything merely on the authority of your teachers and elders. Do not believe in traditions because they have been handed down for many generations. But after observation and analysis, when you find that anything agrees with reason and is conducive to the good and benefit of one and all, then accept it and live up to it.*

▰7-41 As inspirational as the message of his words is, there is another lesson to be learned from Mark Twain: you should always write about what you know. Creating an Ethical Will that comes from the context of your unique perspective not only will make it yours, it is the only thing that will. Even if you choose the words of another to express your thoughts, don't settle for less than language, a tone, a rhythm that feels right when you read it aloud.

▰7-42 ৪০ Books with a message ೧

The average book contains about 75,000 words. Most of you won't tackle a project of that length, but others have and some of them serve as inspiring examples of great stories wrapped around an Ethical Will. Or, are they Ethical Wills wrapped around great stories?

▰7-43 I have already referred to *The Last Lecture*, written by Randy Pausch and Jeffrey Zaslow, as the consummate Ethical Will of book length.[56] It tells the story of Randy Pausch's life and career, revealing the beliefs and values, life lessons and hopes that came from the parents who raised him, the professional peers who mentored him and the loving family who sustained him. More than an autobiography, not quite a memoir, *The Last Lecture* is an Ethical Will.

▰7-44 Anne Morrow Lindbergh, the widow of Charles Lindbergh, was an accomplished aviator, adventurer and best-selling author. Her small book, *Gift from the Sea*, is a series of essays on life, written as she spent isolated time in a beach cabin.[57] Centering each essay on a different type of sea shell, she reflects on her life and the diverse roles of women in our society. You're right—it sounds hokey, but it's not. It's an Ethical Will.

7-45 You already know that Tim Russert's letter to his son Luke is an example of an Ethical Will. In truth, the entire book, *Big Russ and Me*, is an Ethical Will.[58] While speaking of his father and all he learned from being raised by him, Tim Russert artfully includes the essentials of his own Ethical Will and of an Ethical Tribute to his father, Big Russ. *Wisdom of Our Fathers* is a compilation of Ethical Wills by the readers of *Big Russ and Me*.[59] And the beat goes on.

7-46 If you have read Mitch Albom's *Tuesdays with Morrie*,[60] you probably thought you were reading a really great tale, the story of the relationship between a young man and his former professor Morrie as his end of life approaches. Guess what? You were reading an Ethical Will: the message of Morrie Schwartz's beliefs and values, life lessons and hopes for the future.

Here are a few more noteworthy book-length Ethical Wills and/or Ethical Tributes: 7-47 - 7-56

Life Lessons by Elisabeth Kubler-Ross and David Kessler[61]
The Bible by God et al.[62]
Homer's Odyssey by Gwen Cooper[63]
Life on the Mississippi by Mark Twain[64]
The Life and Times of the Thunderbolt Kid by Bill Bryson[65]
This I Believe: The Personal Philosophies of Remarkable
    Men and Women compiled by National Public Radio[66]
have a little faith, a true story by Mitch Albom[67]
The Ultimate Gift by Jim Stovall[68]
Winners Never Cheat – Even in Difficult Times
    by Jon Huntsman[69]
making toast by Roger Rosenblatt[70]

7-57 I speak here about the book as an Ethical Will not because I recommend you write one as your Ethical Will—although if there is a book in you, go for it—but to show how a great story can be more than just a great story. It can have a deep and everlasting message: core beliefs, lessons learned through life experiences and hopes for the future.

When you come across a book that contains the elements of an effective Ethical Will or tells the inspiring story of a life well-lived, recommend it to others. If you have a library of beloved books that you keep because you cannot bear to have their cherished words depart from your home, think long and hard about who should receive their treasured messages when you are gone. Remember

those who can most benefit from the magic and wisdom that is
woven through their pages. Make books a part of your legacy and a
part of your ethical footprint.

_____

_____

📽7-58 *I recall an episode of 3*rd *Rock from the Sun in which the main character Dick
(background: he's from another planet) accuses a fellow professor of plagiarism, noting that every
word of his dissertation had already appeared in another source: the dictionary!*

*There's more than silly humor in that observation. Why not use the words of others if they said
what you wanted to say, just the way you wish you had said it? The creation of your Ethical Will
today might be the reason those words were so well crafted so long ago. What's important is that the
wisdom behind or between those words was spoken in the first place and read and repeated by you.
Give proper credit and the originator will smile, from wherever he or she is.*

End of Chapter Seven

📽7-59

Review - Chapter Seven

- You can create a meaningful Ethical Will without being an experienced writer.
  Quotations from another person may be the best words to convey your message.
- A *first-person quotation* is an expression first spoken by you, or by another, in the
  case of an Ethical Tribute or Ethical Eulogy.
- A *re-quote* is words hand-picked by the subject of the Ethical Will or Ethical Tribute,
  although not original to him or her.
- *Things I wish I'd said* refers to quotations that are fitting to describe a person's value
  system or core beliefs.
- It is possible to sum up a life philosophy in a one-liner, whether original or of
  borrowed words. One-liners can also be used as in embellished quotation, which is
  matching meaningful words with a picture of a special person or place.
- Thumbnail essays are short ethical statements, usually no more than a paragraph.
- An entire book can be an Ethical Will, so you are encouraged to recommend to
  others books with a message and to consider who should receive a bequest of the
  books that have a special place in your life and heart.

Ponder this...
Questions for discussion

1. Do you have a favorite quotation? Please share it and why it resonates with you.

    _____

2. Name a book that spoke to you or had a special message that stayed with you afterwards. What made it so special? Were you surprised at its effect on you?

    _____

3. If you know now, how do you plan to express your Ethical Will? _____

    _____

4. Have you ever considered writing a book? What was your reason? To author a bestseller? To share thoughts with your loved ones? Is that still on your bucket list?

    _____

5. Have you ever thought about what a fitting epitaph would be for you? Have you ever heard or seen one that qualifies as a one-liner Ethical Will?

    _____

    _____

Now, let's exercise our creativity...
Chapter Seven - Exercise 1

Do you have a special book that you have had for a very long time—a book that you just can't let go of? Choose the person who you will pass that book on to and write 75 words to accompany the book: explain why you have treasured it and how it has contributed to your values, wisdom or hopes.

Example:

Little Women by Louisa May Alcott.   It will be passed on to my niece, Katie.

Katie: This book was my mother's (your Grandmother Catherine Kline, for whom you were named), who gave it to me as soon as I was old enough to read it. I have enjoyed it many times and hope that you, too, will let your heart and mind get lost in its stories of loyalty, family teamwork and personal independence.

Now, it's your turn (suggested: 10 minutes/75 words) _____

_____

_____

_____

_____

_____

_____

_____

Chapter Seven - Exercise 2

Choose one of these quotations and then choose someone you think of when you read it. Write for five minutes about how this quotation could be used to describe some aspect of that person's character. Please *show* the reasons, rather than *tell* the reasons.

"I never let my schooling interfere with my education."
- Mark Twain

"Grief is the price we pay for love."
- Queen Elizabeth II

"Time—our youth—it never goes, does it? It is all held in our minds."
- Helen Hooven Santmyer

Example:
"Time—our youth—it never goes, does it? It is all held in our minds."
My BGFF since childhood, Elsbeth Walton. When we get together we giggle just like we did fifty-five years ago. During our infrequent visits (she lives in England), we immediately revert to a comfortable place: our childhood. I'm proud to say that we are still capable of giggling so hard that we snort and we get the same look from strangers that we used to get from our mothers, gazing so proudly at the two of us in Junior Choir.
I'm grateful for this friend who reminds me that with any luck I will never fully mature...

Now, it's your turn (suggested: 15minutes) _____

_____

_____

_____

_____

_____

_____

_____

_____

_____

_____

_____

_____

_____

_____

_____

_____

_____

_____

My songs will pass and be forgotten.
What counts, however, is that I sang them.
Andrew Greeley

℘ **Notes to Self** ℘

Letters are among the most significant memorials
a person can leave behind them.
Johann Wolfgang Von Goethe
📋8-1

📋8-2 ঙ Chapter Eight ল
In your own words

To be honest, that last chapter was there just to give you the confidence to move forward in the belief that you won't have to compose an original message in creating your Ethical Will. But you and I both know that you are capable of writing your own message—if you really want to—and it would really be best if you did even if it's only a short note attached to the prose of another. So, think about what you would say to your loved ones face-to-face, and then consider putting those heartfelt words onto paper.

📋8-3 ঙ A letter ল

As in most things, the simplest method is often the most effective, and when it comes to Ethical Wills, it's a letter. 📋8-4 This book began with my Uncle Bill's simple typed letter to my father. It was full of timeless wisdom and heartfelt guidance from an elder to a younger brother. Creating it did not involve a computer, a digital camera, an audio/visual console or any exceptional technical skills. He used a manual typewriter and a piece of paper (actually, the backside of a church bulletin). You can certainly use word processing software on a computer if you want to easily edit and make multiple copies, but you get the idea. A letter is personal and oh so straightforward.

It was Uncle Bill's message, not the medium, that made it so exceptional. It was a letter meant for one person, containing universal wisdom. It probably took my uncle about an hour to write that letter. Just sixty minutes to create a legacy that has already endured for almost 50 years and will be in the Kline family as a valued treasure for many generations to come.

📋8-5 Do you have just one hour to leave a message that may be the most valuable asset in *your* estate? Think about the elements of your Ethical Will expressed as a letter; think about those who would receive and cherish it, and then find an hour to write your timeless message.

Notes to Self

———————————

———————————

———————————

———————————

———————————

———————————

———————————

———————————

———————————

———————————

———————————

———————————

———————————

———————————

———————————

———————————

———————————

———————————

———————————

———————————

———————————

———————————

✑8-6 ℘ A few well-chosen words ℞

What is any writing but simply a list of words and phrases, skillfully glued together with conjunctions and punctuation? That's simplistic, but if you doubt your ability to make pretty prose, then don't try. Instead, choose the stand alone words that best depict you or another and leave it at that. ✑8-7 From a straightforward catalog of expressions used to describe a person's character, wisdom, personality, temperament, virtue, beliefs, moral fiber, nature or legacy, pluck the ones that apply. It's another way to express an Ethical Will, Ethical Tribute or Ethical Eulogy.

My friend Judi Lodden composed this Ethical Tribute soon after the death of her mother. ✑8-8

What I Learned From My Mom
To have faith
To be patient (she said this was not one of her virtues)
To be optimistic
To be a great cook
To be organized
To know "this too shall pass"
To know "it will be OK"
Wisdom
Reason and common sense
To be assertive
To fight for what is right
To listen
To avoid worrying
To send cards
To laugh heartily and often
To love family and friends
To praise
That happiness is within
To be a good mother, wife and friend
Gregariousness
Spirituality
To trust self
To be intuitive
To have courage
To know that I have a guardian angel
To give of self
To be clear and direct
To be compassionate
To have life balance
To do "all things in moderation"
To have great pride
To be a cheerleader for others

To have strong character and integrity
To be open
To avoid procrastination
To get things done quickly and efficiently
To be trustworthy
To be respectful of others
Thoughtfulness
Mindfulness[71]

This list of words describing Alice Moeckly Springer was born of Judi's grief and then became an everlasting part of her mother's legacy when Judi enclosed a copy with each thank you note sent to friends and family after her mother's death.

🎬8-9 By naming the characteristics that made her mother unique and wonderful, she memorialized the legacy her mother had bequeathed to her loved ones, as gifts and goals. Judi's intent was to give expression to her mother's teachings and the qualities that Judi most missed; she didn't realize she had written what's known as an Ethical Tribute until I told her.

Occasionally, the right word is just beyond my grasp. I know what I want to say, sometimes I even know what letter it starts with, I just can't seem to think of it. 🎬8-10 Where would I be without my thesaurus? I would never expect me to remember all the words I need to express myself and neither should you. 🎬8-11 You will find a list of phrases entitled *"A few well-chosen words"* in the *Appendix*. Try circling a few to describe yourself or another person. A few well-chosen words may be an entire Ethical Will or Ethical Tribute or they can help to focus your thinking for a longer, more complex writing.

🎬8-12 ℘ Personal essays ℧

Unlike a letter, a personal essay is written for a wider audience, perhaps even for publication. Sometimes, when you are very lucky, there is a writing, a personal essay, that says everything one wants to say and can serve as the basis of a wonderful Ethical Will. If it's written by the subject of the Ethical Will (you, perhaps), all the better, but even if written by a third person, it is a gift to find that very special piece that seems to be custom made.

🎬8-13 I got really lucky when I found this essay, written by my Grandmother-in-law May (Murphy) Nelson. It is a poignant accompaniment to these photos of her and her first husband Ernest "Dick" Nelson. 🎬8-14 Grandmother May came by her writing talents naturally: the Murphy women were prodigious adventurers, journalists and photographers. Admittedly, this piece does not include all three core elements of a traditional Ethical Will. However, it is so moving and personal that I cannot imagine not sharing it to reveal how she looked back on one of her most significant life lessons—no doubt an essential part of what made May (Murphy) Nelson such an exceptional person.

▄ 8-15

THE THING I VALUE MOST

When Dick and I were first engaged I sent him my picture. Imagine my surprise when I received a wire the next day saying, "Must have exact duplicate, one not enough." Though greatly puzzled, I sent him another and thereby hangs a tale.

We were married four years before Dick told me why he wanted the two pictures. How well I remember the occasion. We had not gone out that evening but were having one of those wonderful nights at home. We were seated on the divan by the fire--I with my sewing, Dick with his pipe. We were both very much absorbed. Not a sound could be heard, save the patter of rain on the windows. Just the kind of a night for an exchange of confidences.

Finally Dick arose and, going to a drawer, brought out two pictures. Turning to me, he said, "Girl, can you see any difference in these?' and I answered, "Not a particle, except one is horribly soiled while the other is nice and clean." He laughed a little at this remark, and then, drawing me close, with his wonderful arms about me and my head nestled close to his, he repeated the story of his great love for me, the story I had heard from him so many, many times--the only story a woman never grows weary of hearing again and again.

Picking up one of the pictures, he said, "This, I keep looking nice to show my friends. The other", holding up the soiled photo, and here his voice broke, "is the one I worshipped. Those messy looking places are the visible evidence of a boy's love for a girl--the kind of love that overwhelms and envelops you--the lasting kind that has brought us supreme happiness all these years. You will find it covered with finger marks, for I handled it a thousand times. You will find it covered with the marks of tears, when in my great loneliness I lost my self control. And you will find it covered with kisses, the marks of my adoration." For a long time, there was a great silence: he from the embarrassment of his confession, I through sacred awe. This was a new thing to me: I had not known that men did these things.

Today Dick is gone, he lived only another year. And of all my possessions, the thing I value most is an old picture of myself. Anyone else looking at it would see only a battered, badly soiled photo of a girl. To me it is invaluable; nothing could take its place. Every dear old smeared spot has a meaning most tender.

Three months after Dick's death, out of our great love a child was born, a daughter who will never know her father. How much she will cherish this keepsake, a bit of cardboard laying bare a boy's soul; the story of her father's great love for her mother; an old-fashioned photograph of a girl, bearing the imprint of boyish lips and again, the stain of tears, her father's. And mingled with those a woman's tears: her mother's. Could any thing be more beautiful? Could any thing be more sacred? [72]

I have nothing to add to that...

8-16 Prompted by the following prose about animals, it's a good time to talk about the role of our non-human friends and relatives in the world of Ethical Wills and Ethical Tributes. Here are some of my very favorite four-legged family members: [73]

8-17 Stan Rawlinson, the "Doglistener," is a British dog behaviorist and obedience expert. He is also the author of a piece that would partner perfectly with this album page to make an Ethical Will for a beloved pet. I chose it as an Ethical Tribute to my little buddies:

The 10 Commandments From a Pet's Standpoint

1. My life is likely to last 10-15 years, any separation from you will be painful for me. Remember that before you buy me.

2. Give me time to understand what you want from me, don't be impatient, short-tempered, or irritable.

3. Place your trust in me and I will always trust you back. Respect is earned, not given as an inalienable right.

4. Don't be angry with me for long and don't lock me up as punishment, I am not capable of understanding why; I only know I have been rejected. You have your work entertainment and friends. I only have you.

5. Talk to me sometimes. Even if I don't understand your words, I understand your voice and your tone—"you only have to look at my tail."

6. Be aware that however you treat me I'll never forget it, and if it's cruel it may affect me forever.

7. Please don't hit me I can't hit back, but I can bite and scratch and I really don't ever want to do that.

8. Before you scold me for being uncooperative, obstinate, or lazy, ask yourself if something might be bothering me. Perhaps I'm not getting the right foods or I've been out in the sun too long, or my heart is getting old and weak, I may just be dog tired.

9. Take care of me when I get old. You, too, will grow old and may also need love, care, comfort, and attention.

10. Go with me on difficult journeys, never say, "I can't bear to watch" or "Let it happen in my absence." Everything is easier for me if you are there. Remember, irrespective of what you do, I will always love you.[74]

If you don't have pets or are not an animal lover, you might as well skip over this part because you simply will not get it.

🎬8-18 For those of us blessed to share our lives with one, two or a series of dear friends who are of the non-judgmental, unconditional-loving type (by sheer implication, not human), they give more than they get and the examples of their lives are a bounty of meaning and message. They can serve as inspiration for your Ethical Will or as the well-deserved subject of an Ethical Tribute. I would encourage you to record your thoughts about the animals who have shared your life and come to be an integral part of your beliefs and values, life lessons and hopes for the future.

Here's a one-line Ethical Will to get you started: 🎬8-19

Cats seem to go on the principle that
it never does any harm to ask for what you want.
Joseph Wood Krutch

▣ 8-20 ಹಿ **Embellished journals** ಅ

Diaries or journals can be a treasured discipline for the writer as well as the readers privileged to share them. A diary is limited to noting the events of the day and acts as a record of life's milestones, large and small. Writing is usually done on a daily basis, hence the word diary," from the Latin words *diarium*, meaning "daily allowance," *diarius*, meaning "daily" and *dies*, meaning "day."[75] Journaling is a diary on steroids: you may not write every day but when you do, you reflect on life's events and include your thoughts and observations. Throw in the beliefs and values, life lessons and hopes that have sprung from and have been influenced by your experiences, and you've got an Ethical Will in the form of an embellished journal.

A typical diary entry might be: ▣ 8-21

> Dear Diary,
> Today was Christmas. Everyone was here. We had a huge turkey dinner and I ate too much, as usual. This year has flown by and it will be a new one in just a week. Where does the time go?

The same entry in an embellished journal, to someday be shared as your Ethical Will: ▣ 8-22

> Dear Diary,
> Today was Christmas. As we opened our gifts, I looked around the room and thought how very blessed we are to have each other and to be together another year. Even though we had to scale back a bit this year, I think it made us more thoughtful in choosing gifts, and the time we spent making things for each other was priceless.
> Dinner was wonderful, more so because we had so very much to be grateful for: our health, good food, warm shelter, each other.
> I hope and pray that the coming year will be as blessed as this one has been. There are many with much less, and it is our resolution to take the time to appreciate how very blessed we are.

⬛8-23 There is a vast difference between just reporting events and telling how those events affected your beliefs and values, what lessons you learned from looking back on them and how they influenced your outlook going forward.

⬛8-24 Don't be intimidated by the commitment to write, repeat, write, repeat. It does not have to be daily writing—it can weekly, monthly, at holidays, each New Year, on your birthday or on the birthday or anniversary of another person. ⬛8-25 The point is to use an embellished journal to include the core elements of your Ethical Will to show how your reflections evolve over time and to put your beliefs, knowledge and hopes in the context of the life events that mold them.

_____

_____

_____

_____

_____

_____

_____

⬛8-26 *For anyone who thinks he or she can't create an Ethical Will because "I'm not a writer!": when it comes to creating an Ethical Will, the act of watching is more essential than the art of writing.*

End of Chapter Eight
and
Workshop and Slideshow Session II
⬛8-27

Review - Chapter Eight

- You and I both know that you are capable of writing your own message—if you want to—and it would really be best if you did.
- A simple letter, typed or handwritten, can be a treasured family heirloom and it only takes about an hour to write.
- Even a list of adjectives or short phrases can communicate the essence of another in an Ethical Tribute or your own values in an Ethical Will.
- Personal essays are long enough to include storytelling: put your beliefs and values into perspective by giving examples of how you came to learn and adopt those life lessons.
- When it comes to tributes, don't forget your animal friends.
- A diary is a record of events but an embellished journal is a record of what you learned from life's milestones and how your ethical message has grown from your everyday experiences.

Ponder this...
Questions for discussion

1. Do you have any experience as a writer? Have you composed poetry or prose in the past? What did you learn from that experience? _____

_____

_____

2. Do you have any reservations about expressing your Ethical Will "in your own words"? Any thoughts on how you or others can overcome any lingering doubts?

_____

_____

3. Have you ever practiced journaling? If so, how would you go about turning that habit into an embellished journal as part of your ethical message? _____

_____

_____

4. Do you know anyone who has kept a lifelong diary? If so, has he or she shared motivations and hopes for what will ultimately happen to the diaries?

_____

_____

5. If you have pets, have you considered the role they have played in your life and in your family's dynamics? _____

_____

Now, let's exercise our creativity...
Chapter Eight - Exercise 1

Go to Page 133 in the *Appendix* and look at that list of words. If you could use only three words to describe yourself, which three would they be? Choose the three words and then write a sentence for each, giving an example of why you see yourself that way. Be kind—focus on how you want to be remembered (it's okay if one or more of your values or characteristics are not quite fully baked—that's what aspirations are all about...).
(suggested: 10 minutes/3 sentences) _____

_____

_____

_____

_____

_____

_____

_____

_____

Chapter Eight - Exercise 2

Starring *you* again: You have 15 minutes to describe yourself to the world. Before you write, think about the parts of your life that you are most proud of, what you hope will be your legacy and will live on long after you are gone. **(suggested: 15 minutes)**

_____

_____

_____

_____

_____

_____

_____

_____

_____

_____

_____

_____

_____

_____

_____

_____

_____

_____

_____

_____

_____

_____

_____

_____

_____

_____

_____

_____

_____

_____

_____

_____

Do not forget the things your eyes have seen
or let them slip from your heart as long as you live.
Teach them to your children and your children's children.
Deuteronomy 4:9

৩ **Notes to Self** ৫

One of the great joys of life is creativity.
Information goes in, gets shuffled about, and
comes out in new and interesting ways.
Peter McWilliams

℘ Notes to Self ℘

🎬9-1 <u>WORKSHOP and SLIDESHOW SESSION III</u>

If you hear a voice within you say 'you cannot paint,'
then by all means paint and that voice will be silenced.
Vincent Van Gogh
🎬9-2

🎬9-3 ℬ Chapter Nine ℭ
Three-dimensional Ethical Wills

The first Ethical Will, the one delivered by Jacob on his death bed, was written with a stylus and a clay tablet about 100 years after its telling. We now have media that weighs a lot less and it doesn't take two months for twenty indentured servants to make copies for the cousins. Even better, an Ethical Will need not be limited to mere words. 🎬9-4 If you are already familiar with digital photography, scrapbooking, genealogy or cooking, you can incorporate your creative talents with the message of your beliefs, lessons and hopes to craft a unique multi-faceted Ethical Will or Ethical Tribute.

🎬9-5 ℬ An embellished photo album ℭ

When asked what possession they would grab if the house was burning, most people say, "the photo albums!" With the onset of digital photography, they might say "the computer!" Either way, pictures measure the passage of time as well as capturing the special moments of our lives. 🎬9-6 When a loved one has passed on, a photo that portrays his or her special smile or expression is priceless. But it's just another photo album with fading photos that call to mind fading memories until you bring alive the essence of those pictured in it with words of reflection. Then, it's an embellished photo album—an Ethical Tribute.

🎬9-7 In this age of one-upping everything, an "embellished" photo album, journal or scrapbook usually refers to including bits of decoration, artful mats or fanciful borders. 🎬9-8 In the world of Ethical Wills, however, "embellished" means to add words to a journal, photo album, scrapbook, genealogy or cookbook to illustrate one or more of the core elements of an Ethical Will or Ethical Tribute.

Notes to Self

_____
_____
_____
_____
_____
_____
_____
_____
_____
_____
_____
_____
_____
_____
_____
_____
_____
_____
_____
_____
_____

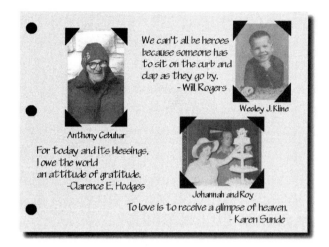

We can't all be heroes
because someone has
to sit on the curb and
clap as they go by.
- Will Rogers

Wesley J. Kline

Anthony Cebuhar

For today and its blessings,
I owe the world
an attitude of gratitude.
-Clarence E. Hodges

Johannah and Roy
To love is to receive a glimpse of heaven.
- Karen Sunde

⬛9-9 These are three of my favorite people, no longer with us, and quotations that capture a small part of each spirit.[76] The phrases or quotations you choose can refer to a quality of the person pictured or it can describe the influence that life had on your own.

Unfortunately, I never got to meet Hannah (Smith) Kline,[77] the paternal grandmother for whom I am named. She is a fascinating enigma to me, with a face so sweet, belying the strong spirit she was known for and obviously bequeathed to her many descendants. And I think she looks just slightly peeved in this picture, which makes her even more intriguing.

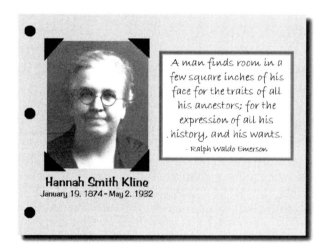

A man finds room in a
few square inches of his
face for the traits of all
his ancestors; for the
expression of all his
history, and his wants.
- Ralph Waldo Emerson

Hannah Smith Kline
January 19, 1874 - May 2, 1932

Back to Boone, Iowa, where I spent countless childhood weekends with my maternal grandmother, Elizabeth (Hardie) Jones, walking uptown for a few groceries or making a craft at her dining table. Since I was very young, I have kept a yellowed slip of paper that Grandma Jones mailed to my home in Des Moines. She was a woman of few words herself (she always greeted others with "How do?" and a nod), but she came across these poems and passed them on to me. Being the God-fearing woman that she was, I would guess they were cut from a church bulletin. It may have lacked originality, but Grandma was certainly thinking creatively when she gifted these words to me.[78] It seems a fitting Ethical Tribute to place them alongside her picture.

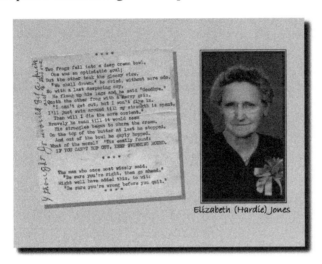

Elizabeth (Hardie) Jones

⬛9-10 Sometimes one finds a newspaper or magazine clipping, a story or a poem tucked in the pages of the family Bible or in a handkerchief drawer, placed there decades ago by someone who found the words inspirational or amusing. It's like sharing a special moment, separated only by time (which is, after all, as Mr. Einstein made very clear, relative). Such a treasure might be just the thing to accompany a photo of that ancestor and to reveal a bit about the person pictured there.

⬛9-11 Any one of these embellished album pages could be part of an Ethical Genealogy or an Ethical Will slideshow: pictures of the people who have been important and influential in your life or tree of life, sprinkled with a quotation to epitomize each one. You can have the pages of an existing photo album scanned, allowing you to add your thoughts, handwritten or digitally. Or you can remove the pictures, scan them and put copies into an archival album with words of tribute next to each. See the *Appendix* for information on using archival supplies and procedures to preserve original heirloom documents.

⬛9-12 Please be sure to put the name and any other relevant information either alongside the Ethical Tribute or on the back of each picture. Actually, doing both would be best. In the practice of gathering and recording family history, little is more heartbreaking than having a box or album of your ancestors' faces looking back at you, and not having a clue about who they are.

⬛9-13 ᔕ **An embellished scrapbook** ᓚ

This section warrants its own glossary, so first let's get hip to the lingo: ⬛9-14

Scrapping or Scrappin': creating a scrapbook
Crop: 1) to trim photos and 2) to gather with friends to create scrapbooks. Example: "I'll be cropping some photos at next week's crop."
Memorabilia: historical items used in a scrapbook such as photos and clippings.
Embellishments: items used to decorate the pages of a scrapbook such as ribbons, stickers or rubber stamps.[79]

⬛9-15 Until the 1980s, scrapbooking meant using the most awful-tasting lumpy paste (how is it we all know that?) to glue photos, die-cut art, ticket stubs, invitations, news clippings, greeting cards, party favors, ribbons, magazine cut outs and any other loose reminders of family, friends and social life onto the pages of an unwieldy book. It was usually held together by a string meant to allow the addition of pages as the scrapbook grew. ⬛9-16 My friend since our births one month apart, Elsbeth "Buff" Walton, has 30 scrapbooks that her mother, Dorothea "Dot" Walton, created on her behalf (two brothers each have a similar collection). Her mother—whose own delightful obsession with miniatures fostered mine—had 50 of her own. ⬛9-17 My mother Catherine Kline, dear friends with Dot since they were young women, filled many scrapbooks with her mementoes. As for me, I was a slacker, a piker and a no-show. I wasn't all that disciplined or interested and never needed to add to my scrapbooks because I never filled even one. Maybe I would have been more respectful of the tradition if I'd realized at the time that we practicing a 500-year-old art form.

⬛9-18 Beginning in the 1400s, *commonplace books* were used in England to collect all sorts of memorabilia, including poems, recipes and letters. In 1775, James Granger added blank pages to the end of a book on the history of England, ready to receive the personal mementoes of the reader, much like the *Notes to Self* pages in this book. Who knew I was *grangerizing*?[80]
⬛9-19 Thomas Jefferson,[81] Lewis Carroll[82] and Mark Twain (who even patented a "self-pasting" scrapbook in 1872),[83] joined the ranks of people somewhat obsessed with creating countless volumes filled with their personal histories. ⬛9-20 Then the 1980s brought a plethora of background papers, templates, weird pinking shears, fancy borders, photo mats, buttons, bows, rubber stamps, artful punches, stencils and personal die-cut machines. The art of scrapbooking is now a multimillion dollar industry, complete with specialized stores, packaged supplies and—I can only hope—

☙9-21 support groups to embrace those for whom scrapping has become a "problem."

☙9-22 With all that history in mind, consider using the concept of a scrapbook to bring together the best elements of an Ethical Will: the memories, images and words that represent the values, lessons and hopes that are yours or a loved one's.

☙9-23 Here is a scrapbook page that includes photos of my late husband Roy Z. Fort (was he a cute baby or what?), along with his family members: sister Faith Ann, mother Helen and father Walt. I have included the invitation to our wedding and a poem that was meaningful to me when Roy passed away in 1979. It is a bittersweet collection of memories that communicates the importance of Roy's life: the deep affection he had for his family and his attitude about carrying on even though he is no longer physically with us.[84]

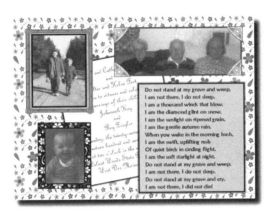

☙9-24 Milestone birthdays or anniversaries are particularly appropriate times to create an embellished scrapbook, filled with memories of people, places and events and your reflections on each, considering the values, lessons and hopes that came from them.

This scrapbook page includes my parents' wedding certificate and photos of them, just married and 30 years later, and a fitting quotation.[85] The background is a street scene from their hometown of Boone, Iowa.

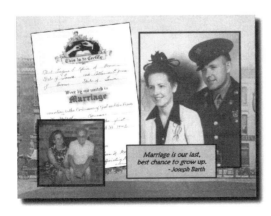

9-25 Your impressions of an ancestor don't have to come from actually having known him or her. The poem, quotation or prose that you include in an Ethical Scrapbook can be a reflection of secondhand stories about the person or your thoughts on his or her significance in your family tree.

9-26 Earlier I spoke of the importance of photographs among the stuff that we seem to collect. Why not sort all those pictures that are now in envelopes and shoe boxes, focus on a few that depict your loved ones as you choose to remember them, along with the wedding invitations, locks of baby hair, newspaper clippings, favorite poems, songs or quotations and assemble a priceless family treasure?

9-27 ℘ An embellished genealogy ℘

9-28 A family tree is just a database of the birth and death statistics of your ancestors and descendants until you add stories, quotations and remembrances of each person's essence and what makes him or her a unique and unforgettable member of your family. With the advancement of sophisticated genealogical software, it is simple to scan photographs and important documents as well as your notations on the people we lovingly refer to as *relatives*.

9-29 Now would be a good time to jot down the stories that you remember about family members who are no longer here. Ask other relatives to do the same (it's a tale in itself to witness the different perspectives on the same person or event). Don't concern yourself with style or even format, just get them recorded and worry later about how you will use them—what's important is to mine your sources while they are still available. 9-30 Then plan to insert them into the family history when you start to enter the basic information on your "twigs" and "leaves." Another elephant being eaten in small bites: if you make it a goal to record two or three relatives every day or so, you will have the tree done in no time. (Of course, that doesn't apply if you're one of the Klines, but I suppose there has to be some disadvantage to being from such a ginormous family.)

9-31 Many software packages can automatically create a "family book" from the materials you upload and the Ethical Tributes that you create will be a part of that record. 9-32 It takes us back to the sentiment of *"As the twig is bent, so grows the tree."* For generations to come, not yet born, a family history that shows what ancestors believed, knew to be true and hoped for is a rare opportunity to witness the values woven through our families and our familial ideals, both fulfilled and aspired to.

▰9-33 ℘ An embellished cookbook ℭ

▰9-34 I am in the third generation of the Kline family begun by John and Hannah. We're now well into the fifth layer and nobody puts on a family reunion like the Klines. There are lots of cousins (two of them once got into a playground fight—they didn't realize they were related) and lots of good cooks. My cousin (first, once removed) Susie (Peterson) Sharp has wisely relocated the biennial gathering to its original site, a shelter at McHose Park in Boone, Iowa. The park is a stone's throw from Linwood Park Cemetery, where John and Hannah Kline now reside with contemporaries and descendants so it's handy to visit their graves before starting the second dessert course.

▰9-35 Amid antique picnic tables laden with potluck dishes, we "walk the line," tasting the selection of family recipes. The assortment only serves to prove my irrefutable Random Potluck Matrix Theory: although food categories are never assigned, there is always a flawless distribution of veggies, fried chicken, meatloaf, desserts and—of course—Jell-O salads. But I digress.

▰9-36 Food is a big part of life in America which makes it a big part of our history and the legacy of those who have gone before. So, how about styling an Ethical Genealogy on the recipes of a family? My goal is to someday coordinate a collection of Kline family recipes along with the stories of those who first made those tasty contributions. ▰9-37 Witness my Aunt Isabel (McCollum) Kline and her Chicken Divan (pronounced Chicken "Die-van").[86]

Although it has been updated with the addition of artichoke hearts and grated Italian five cheeses, it is still the elegant comfort food that Aunt Isabel served 50 years ago to an endless parade of bridge players and bridal shower invitees. It somehow epitomizes her talents as a gracious hostess and faultless entertainer. She practiced the true meaning of manners and hospitality: to make others feel comfortable.

An embellished cookbook brings together the best of the people, memories and foods that make each family unique. It is also an Ethical Will format that will be made richer by many contributors with a variety of memories and stories. An Ethical Will cookbook as a multigenerational project is an ambitious venture that will be a treasured family heirloom forever.

You can't possibly write an Ethical Will? Okay, can you write a paragraph about your Grandmother and the smell of her Christmas cookies baking? I thought so.

*9-38 Maybe you've been meaning to sort those old photographs or recipes or put together a scrapbook or finish your 40-year-old daughter's baby book? You can do more than just assemble pictures and scraps if you add the thoughts and meaning of an Ethical Will: *9-39 beliefs, lessons and hopes.*

End of Chapter Nine
*9-40

Review - Chapter Nine

- An Ethical Will can be expressed by embellishing other "memory media": the ways in which we memorialize the people and the stories of our lives.
- A family photo album can serve as an Ethical Tribute to those pictured by adding words about their beliefs and values, life lessons and hopes for the future.
- Scrapbooks hold the bits and pieces of our lives. Include words about the values, lessons and hopes of those events, people and places and you have an Embellished Scrapbook.
- Genealogy is the history of your family. An embellished genealogy includes stories about ancestors that demonstrate their values, wisdom and hopes. Remember: when your ancestors talked about their hopes for the world of the future, that was you they were dreaming about...
- American life is all about eating. What better way to talk about our family members and loved ones than to record thoughts about their favorite foods and the special memories and lessons that surround those recipes?

Ponder this...
Questions for discussion

1. Do you have a vintage family photo album? Do you know the identity of each person pictured in it? If not, do you have any living relatives who can help you with that? _____

   _____

2. Have you had the experience of finding a newspaper clipping or poem tucked away by an ancestor? Speculate about the circumstances that led them to keep that particular memento or the "coincidence" of you finding it.

   _____

   _____

3. Have you ever made a scrapbook? If so, do you remember what you included?

   _____

   _____

   _____

4. Do you have any letters belonging to an ancestor? Have you read them? Might they be the beginning of an Ethical Genealogy?_____

   _____

   _____

5. Raise your hand if you have a favorite family recipe that is a crowd-pleaser—just making it or eating it makes you smile. What is it? Do you ever make it?

   _____

   _____

Now, let's exercise our creativity...
Chapter Nine - Exercise 1

Picture an embellished scrapbook page of your life as it is right now. List five artifacts you would include and, for each one, write a few words about why you included it. What does each memento say about your values, life lessons or hopes? (For example, a wedding invitation, a dried corsage, a graduation or birth announcement, an obituary.)
(suggested: 10 minutes) _____

_____

_____

_____

_____

_____

_____

_____

_____

_____

_____

Chapter Nine - Exercise 2

Name the family recipe or food that first comes to mind. Think about why you chose it. Why do you love it so much? If you don't come from a family of cooks, what food do you really enjoy—a true "comfort" food to you? (How about making it your family's tradition?) Either way, tell why you chose that recipe and talk about the family traditions or memories that it makes you think of or that you hope it will come to mean to others? **(suggested: 5 minutes)** _____

_____

_____

_____

_____

_____

_____

_____

_____

_____

_____

_____

_____

_____

_____

_____

_____

_____

_____

_____

_____

_____

_____

_____

Want to make your computer go really fast?
Throw it out a window.
Anonymous
◉10-1

◉10-2 ☙ Chapter Ten ❧
Reasons to love your computer

Historically, I have had a love-hate relationship with the computer. Not *my* computer, mind you. The relationship between my computer and me is all lovey-dovey. It's sort of like attorneys and congressmen. If you ask people to rate either profession in general, they put them in the company of telemarketers. *But* ask about their own attorney or congressman, and they're in line next to the family clergy. My computer and I are totally simpatico, mostly because I could never have written this book without the use of computer-generated research and computer-generated layout tools and computer-generated presentations to talk about the computer-generated manuscript—and my computer knows it.

Yes, it's computers in general that I do not trust. And I know many of you feel the same. We are intimidated by their intelligence, regardless of how artificial it may be. And I would never suggest that you add bells and whistles to an Ethical Will, Ethical Eulogy or Ethical Tribute simply because you can. I just ask that you open your mind to the possibility that a computer—yours or that of a loved one such as a small child or grandchild—can play an important role in taking an Ethical Will beyond mere words on paper or even in an album or scrapbook. The message can become multidimensional and multimedia, making an Ethical Will even more reflective of one's personal style and essence and even more unforgettable.

◉10-3 ☙ Digiscrapbooks ❧

I wasn't completely forthright when I shared the miniglossary of scrapbooking terms in *Chapter Nine*. I was afraid you would not read further if I included this one: ◉10-4

Digiscrapping: creating a scrapbook on a computer with the aid of digitized images as the elements of the scrapbook.[87]

Notes to Self

_____
_____
_____
_____
_____
_____
_____
_____
_____
_____
_____
_____
_____
_____
_____
_____
_____

▰10-5 True confession: the scrapbook pages in *Chapter Nine* exist only in my imagination and on my computer. The same is true for the embellished photo album and embellished cookbook. There is no cardboard and paper scrapbook with pictures of Roy or my parents or the recipe for Chicken Divan. The only place these images have existed until now is on my computer's monitor. But I can easily bring them to three-dimensional reality: all I have to do is print those images and assemble a traditional scrapbook or cookbook. ▰10-6 The point is, I would probably not have taken the time or effort to assemble all the materials I needed to create those pages in the old-fashioned way, but it was easy to do using digitized photos and borders and backgrounds. ▰10-7 There is a myriad of software programs available that make digiscrapping so easy that choosing between the many design elements will be the most difficult task. Or you can use familiar programs such as Microsoft Publisher or PowerPoint to do the same, pulling in clip art from a variety of sources.[88]

Once your collection of photos is scanned, you can manipulate it to your heart's desire before deciding which version to print. ▰10-8 Consider the limitless possibilities for format and design once you can easily resize photographs, adjust color, crop out unwanted scenery (or people) or zoom in to frame just one face in a group picture. By adding scanned copies of family documents and text, you can craft a digiscrapbook, digiphotoalbum, digicookbook or digi-geneology as your Ethical Will. (Or find a small child to do it for you.)

▰10-9 ℰℴ **PowerPoint slideshows** ℭℛ

They said I would never move past overhead transparencies and then I discovered PowerPoint, and my public speaking was never the same. ▰10-10 If your experience with PowerPoint has been trying to cipher too many words that are too tiny on a screen that is too far away, fuggedaboudit. For the audience, a bad PowerPoint presentation is frustrating and a distraction to the speaker's message, so let's not do that. ▰10-11 What I am suggesting is the use of Microsoft's PowerPoint software to create a multi-media Ethical Will that incorporates faces, places, text, voices and even music. ▰10-12 PowerPoint also provides a way to share your Ethical Will with others by means other than showing it on a screen with a projector: you can e-mail a PowerPoint presentation as an attachment or distribute copies downloaded onto CDs or flash drives.

▰10-13 This slide from one of my PowerPoint Ethical Wills has only three components:

- the background design (free clipart, with a nod to Bill Gates)
- two photo images from scanning the original snapshots
- a text box containing the Longfellow quotation (a PowerPoint function with two clicks).

The simplest of PowerPoint slideshows is a series of pictures, strung together with quotations and even background music. Once a template slide is created, adding photos and text to each is not all that complicated. Really.

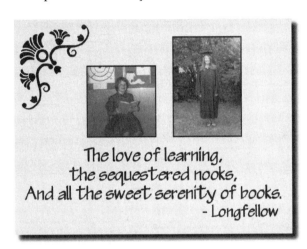

Again, I would suggest that those of you who are not computer-savvy—and do not want to be—find the nearest family member, friend, neighbor or small child who is willing to help you assemble the components. (Great way for your techy granddaughter to earn while she learns.) Those photos of yesteryear can be scanned and then resized, recolored or cropped.

≤10-14 My Ethical Will (one of them) consists of 14 slides, 18 photos, 12 quotes and is about three minutes long. As with any other Ethical Will, the yeoman's work is getting organized. ≤10-15 Once you have selected the photos, quotations, text, poems, essays, music or voices that best convey your message, creating a slideshow is simply a matter of draggin' and droppin' (computer lingo for picking it up from one place and putting it down in another place). Go for it.

≤10-16 ℘ Video recordings ℃

For the personal touch, nothing beats the facial expressions and voice of the person behind an Ethical Will. ≤10-17 Randy Pausch's *Last Lecture,*[89] as delivered at Carnegie Mellon, is a one-hour sixteen-minute DVD, full of personal reflections and timeless wisdom. Watching this endearing young man do pushups and surprise his wife with a birthday cake on stage cannot be communicated without the audiovisuals. Perhaps your Ethical Will would also be best expressed as a video.

📹10-18 Who doesn't have a video camera these days or know someone who does? I would encourage you to make a video of senior members of your family, using the core elements of an Ethical Will. Stories of special childhood memories intertwined with beliefs, lessons and hopes, will have a well-deserved place in the family archives.

📹10-19 As you will learn in *Chapter Eleven*, to foster effective communication, every Ethical Will, no matter how simple or complex, must start with an outline. That is especially true if it is a video or audio recording. The message will surely be lost if the speaker is allowed to adopt a stream-of-consciousness format. Even if the message is still intact—buried in there somewhere—the audience will not be. Narrowing the focus with guiding questions or a written outline of key messages will keep the script relevant and the speaker on point.

📹10-20 In *Chapter Eleven*, there is a simple outline for a basic Ethical Will, and there is a detailed format based on Max Ehrmann's timeless poem *Desiderata* in *Chapter Twelve*. You can follow either one to decide which core elements to include before going in front of the camera. A monologue in which the speaker simply delivers his or her message or a dialogue in which a second person is either on- or off-camera prompting the speaker with questions can be used. Remember that the computer is your friend and it is not difficult for someone to edit the video once you are done. You can then add title and credit slides (a good place to note who the speaker is and the date of the interview), music, photos and adjust the volume.

📹10-21 To learn about the consummate video Ethical Will project, visit the Charles E. Smith Life Communities website and discover their "Lessons of a Lifetime, the Ethical Will Project of the Hebrew Home." Trained student volunteers work with residents to produce videos that archive stories and wisdom, creating invaluable personal histories and Ethical Wills.[90]

Have fun with this method. It enables you to include humor and a truly personal tone in an Ethical Will. 📹10-22 Does anything reveal a person's essence more clearly than the face? The smile? I don't think so, either.

📹10-23 ೞ **Audio recordings** ೞ

You'd like to create an up-front and personal Ethical Will, but a video camera is just a little too intimidating? How about an audio recording? You may forget that little microphone is even present.

≝10-24 Capture the voice, the laughter, the dialect, the tone, the accent, the special timbre that makes each voice unique and recognizable. ≝10-25 This is an opportunity as well for senior members of your family to relate memories of the family homestead, speak of ancestors long gone or to identify mystery photos. What I would give to have a recording of the special people in my life who are no longer here.

Equipment can be as simple as an inexpensive microphone plugged into your computer and editing software. Many versions are available online at no cost.[91]

≝10-26 All that I said about making a video applies to an audio recording as well. Have an outline or prompting questions in front of the speaker. Winging it will result in a message that is lost in the flotsam. ≝10-27 Either video or audio can be edited for content later, but it is always best to make sure the most important points, the key messages, get covered and an outline is the only way to do that.

≝10-28 An audio recording is a throwback to the first known Ethical Will: Jacob's oral blessing to his loved ones. A spoken Ethical Will still works as an irreplaceable message that reflects the person's beliefs and values, life lessons and hopes for the future.

≝10-29 ℘ The language of music ℆

Music is a powerful communicator. Hearing a song associated with an extraordinary moment or event in your past has the power to change your mood in an instant, to leave you smiling or sobbing. It can appear like a messenger from another time, jolting our senses and making us believe we are there. Not surprisingly, music can play a fundamental role in the creation of an Ethical Will. In truth, the right lyrics and/or melody can *be* an Ethical Will. If you have a favorite song, listen to the words and you may find that the lyrics have a place in your Ethical Will or that of a loved one.

≝10-30 ♫ Turn Turn Turn ♫
To everything, Turn turn turn
There is a season, Turn turn turn.
And a time to every purpose, under Heaven.[92]

≝10-31 ♫ Deep Peace ♫
Deep peace of the running wave to you;
Deep peace of the flowing air to you;
Deep peace of the quiet earth to you;
Deep peace of the shining stars to you.[93]

🎬10-32 🎵 **Now and Forever** 🎵
Now and forever, you are a part of me
And the memory cuts like a knife
Didn't we find the ecstasy
Didn't we share the daylight
When you walked into my life.[94]

If a favorite tune does not have perfectly appropriate lyrics that can stand alone, the song itself may represent your outlook on life or how you would like to be remembered.

🎬10-33 🎵 **On the Sunny Side of the Street** 🎵
Grab your coat—don't forget your hat,
But leave your worries—leave 'em on the doorstep.
Life's sweet—just direct your feet
to the sunny sunny side of the street.[95]

🎬10-34 🎵 **Dream a Little Dream of Me** 🎵
Stars shining bright above you
Night breezes seem to whisper "I love you"
Birds singing in the sycamore tree
Dream a little dream of me.[96]

In a PowerPoint, video, or audio Ethical Will, music can be the introduction, the background or the ending notes. 🎬10-35 If dancing was an important or memorable part of your life, using a tango as accompaniment will bring a smile, alongside the photos and/or words. For the person who played a musical instrument, background music featuring that instrument would serve double duty. My favorite example is that of my late friend Susan (Dunham) Bjorkgren whose husband Craig (B. J.) found a 35-year-old recording of Sue's college music final—she was a gifted vocalist—just prior to the day of her memorial. Her voice filled the church as her friends and family gathered. It was an unexpected and incredible blessing.

Perhaps the melody alone is the message, setting a mood and tone to accompany words of poetry or prose.

🎬10-36 🎵 **Four Seasons, Opus 8 No. 1 (Vivaldi)** 🎵[97]

🎬10-37 🎵 **Adagio for Strings, Opus 11 (Barber)** 🎵[98]

🎬10-38 🎵 **We're in the Club Now (Giacchino)** 🎵[99]

If you explore the use of music as part of your Ethical Will, be aware of the potential effect on the listener. 🎬10-39 I know of one orchestral piece that is exceptionally beautiful. It is also the theme song from the movie *An Affair to Remember,* so probably not a good choice for an Ethical Will.

For some songs, the words are so familiar that you can use an instrumental version of the song without the lyrics and still have the desired effect.

🎬10-40 🎵 As Time Goes By 🎵

You must remember this:
A kiss is still a kiss, a sigh is just a sigh.
The fundamental things apply
As time goes by.[100]

🎬10-41 🎵 Somewhere Over the Rainbow 🎵

Somewhere over the rainbow, way up high
There's a land that I heard of once in a lullaby.
Somewhere over the rainbow,
Skies are blue and the dreams that you dare to dream
Really do come true.[101]

Effective communication is key to an effective Ethical Will, so be wary of choosing music that is a distraction or conflicts with the other media you may be using. You will want any tune to enhance—not detract from—your presentation. 🎬10-42 Don't use music that confuses or over stimulates your audience. For instance, using music with lyrics could serve as a harmful distraction as the background of a slideshow featuring quotations.

When you consider its effect, recognize that the same piece of music can have dramatically different effects, depending on the version and the perspective of the audience.

🎬10-43 🎵 When You Wish Upon a Star 🎵

When you wish upon a star
Makes no difference who you are
Anything your heart desires
Will come to you. [102]

🎬10-44 As sung by Cliff Edwards, Jiminy Cricket in the 1940 Disney movie *Pinocchio,* this song may evoke sweet memories of seeing that movie for the first time as a child or of the adult who treated you to it. Sung by the Mormon Tabernacle Choir, it becomes a contemporary spiritual, with a message of hope and dream fulfillment. 🎬10-45

Religious or sacred music is often the first choice in a conventional memorial or funeral setting. It may also be appropriate for an Ethical Eulogy, but consider whether it sets the right tone before including it in an Ethical Will.

◉10-46 ♫ It Is Well With My Soul ♫

When peace, like a river, attendeth my way,
When sorrows like sea billows roll;
Whatever my lot, Thou has taught me to say,
It is well, it is well, with my soul. [103]

This song has a message that could easily be part of an Ethical Eulogy or an Ethical Will and so do both of these popular songs:

◉10-47 ♫ Spirit In the Sky ♫

When I die and they lay me to rest
Gonna go to the place that's the best
When I lay me down to die
Goin' up to the spirit in the sky. [104]

◉10-48 ♫ Circle of Life (The Lion King) ♫

From the day we arrive on the planet
And, blinking, step into the sun
There's more to see than can ever be seen
More to do than can ever be done. [105]

Music creates a mood—intentional or otherwise—wherever it is heard and being part of an Ethical Will is no exception. ◉10-49 If you decide to include music in an Ethical presentation, make your selection with this in mind: does it enhance the message of your essence and what you stand for?

◉10-50 ◈ Miscellaneous media ◈

If you didn't see your favorite hobby or craft listed in these four chapters, it just means that I don't know about it yet. I invite you to keep your mind open to all possible media for an Ethical Will. ◉10-51 Recently, I discovered "memory jugs" which are simple homemade projects, made to honor a person by embellishing stoneware or a bottle with personal mementoes. It is believed they were first made as grave markers for African-American cemeteries in the South or were perhaps a product of the Victorian scrapbooking mania. [106]

Originally, they were made by covering the container with clay and then embedding items that belonged to the person being honored: keys, charms, earring, buttons, medals, small toys, shells and—yes—even teeth. Using modern modeling clay, a memory jug on a small scale could be a way to introduce the idea of an Ethical Will to children. Remember to accompany any memory jug with a list of the items adorning it and the significance of each to really make it a message in a bottle (get it?). Sorry.

📹10-52 Likewise, there are "memory quilts" that are usually a group effort, each block with an inspiring thought and a name stitched into it. Sounds like an ambitious but precious heirloom project for a family in recognition of a milestone birthday, anniversary or reunion.

📹10-53 How about Ethical Calling Cards? I met a woman who has prepared business card-sized mementoes for distribution at her well-planned memorial service. Each one contains a pithy quote of life philosophy or Irish humor (she'll "be wanting to save the belly laughs for the burial").[107]

📹10-54 Or the astonishing blessing I received recently just after a friend passed away unexpectedly. I got a glimpse into her everyday reflections on life and her philosophy of acceptance by reviewing the inspiring notes she had been posting on her Facebook wall just prior to her passing.

True, there is a limit to the number of ways that an Ethical Will can be expressed, but since humans can't grasp the concept of infinity, it's of no matter. 📹10-55 As Henry David Thoreau said, *"This world is but a canvas to our imaginations."*

Yikes! Before I started writing these four chapters, even I had no idea there are so many ways to express the message of an Ethical Will. As fun as it is to see all the possibilities, keep in mind that the medium of an Ethical Will is just that: a technique to communicate the core elements of the message. What's important is that you find a means, however simple or multifaceted, that motivates you to record your bequest of values. 📹10-56 No matter what form it takes, the significance of an Ethical Will is sharing what you believe, what you know and what you hope for.

Perhaps you should go back now and review the past four chapters and consider which idea would be most fun, most fulfilling and—not unimportantly—most likely to be completed by you. Keep thinking about that...

End of Chapter Ten
📹10-57

Review - Chapter Ten

- Computer software allows you to create a multidimensional Ethical Will that can make your ethical message even more unforgettable.
- A digiscrapbook is computer generated by layering scanned images of photos, invitations, important documents, recipes or even handwritten letters.

- A Powerpoint slideshow is no longer a medium solely for professional presenters. It is a way to combine images, words, music or narration in a format that is portable and transferrable.
- Any camcorder can be the means to make a video Ethical Will. Following an outline keeps the speaker on message while communicating unique facial expressions, body language and voice.
- A simple tape recorder or microphone plugged into your computer can make a priceless record of you or a loved one's voice and ethical message.
- It may be the melody, the lyrics or even the type of instrument that makes a piece of music the perfect expression of your Ethical Will.
- Use your imagination to discover other ways to express the unique message of what you believe, know and hope for. A memory jug, memory quilt, message cards or even your Facebook page can be a way to memorialize your ethical message.

Ponder this...
Questions for discussion

1. Do you have the computer skills you need to create a digital Ethical Will? Are those skills you would like to acquire or sharpen? Brainstorm ideas for help with using a computer in expressing your Ethical Will (tutorials, classes, a grandchild, neighbor, someone you can barter with—a pan of brownies goes a long way with a college student).

   _____
   _____
   _____
   _____

2. Have you ever seen a Powerpoint slideshow that was spectacular or one that flopped? What was it about those presentations that did or did not work?

   _____
   _____
   _____

3. Have you ever been involved in creating a memory quilt or similar item for a special anniversary or milestone birthday celebration? If so, what did you learn about your family or group of loved ones from that experience?

   _____
   _____
   _____
   _____

4. Do you play a musical instrument or used to in younger days? Talk about ways you might incorporate that instrument or other music into your Ethical Will.

   _____
   _____
   _____

5. Can you think of any other unique or unusual ways to express an Ethical Will that were not mentioned in *SO GROWS THE TREE*? If so, please share.

_____

_____

_____

Now, let's exercise our creativity...
Chapter Ten - Exercise 1

Make a music selection from the examples in this chapter or choose another song that you know well (if you are using the lyrics, please write them here). In 100 words or less, tell why you chose that song, focusing on how it helps to express the values, life lessons or hopes contained in your Ethical Will. **(suggested: 15 minutes/100 words)**

_____

_____

_____

_____

_____

_____

_____

_____

_____

_____

_____

_____

_____

Chapter Ten - Exercise 2

Imagine you are going to produce a Powerpoint slideshow as your Ethical Will. Design just <u>two</u> of the slides. Each one should include one or more items that express the elements of your ethical message: a photo, a quotation, a song in the background, a special document, such as a birth certificate or wedding invitation. Let your imagination do most of the work here: jot down the ideas as quickly as they come to you and worry about editing later! **(suggested: 10 minutes/2 slides)**

_____

_____

_____

Art is the desire of a man to express himself,
to record the reactions
of his personality to the world he lives in.
Amy Lowell

ಕಾ Notes to Self ಇ

◖11-1 Part III.
Your journey begins with a single step

Organizing is what you do before you do something,
so that when you do it, it is not all mixed up.
Alan Alexander Wilne
◖11-2

◖11-3 ℘ Chapter Eleven ℘
How to get started

Notes to Self

For a moment, let's revisit the basics. An Ethical Will has three essential elements:

◖11-4 **Beliefs and values.**   These are the core values and principles that have served you well throughout your life. They consistently prove to be trustworthy and to operate as a reliable moral compass, no matter what the trial or circumstances. *Character, principles, reputation, integrity, life philosophy, ideals, credo.*

◖11-5 **Life lessons.** Life lessons are the principles you know to be true that are learned in just one place: the School of Hard Knocks. *Experience, stories, reflections, observations, advice, wisdom.*

◖11-6 **Hopes for the future.**   The world tomorrow will not be the same as today—that's for sure. Your Ethical Will is the place to hope for the best and the opportunity to envision a future where all the wishes for you and for those you love come true. Nothing can exist until it is first imagined. *Dreams, aspirations, objectives, goals, wishes.*

◖11-7 Approach the writing of your Ethical Will with these core elements in mind.   What is it you want to cover and not forget to include in your Ethical Will? What are the essentials of your story? Your message? Your philosophy? As you have seen from many examples of Ethical Wills, you can include all three elements or just two or just one. It's entirely up to you.

◖11-8 First, no writing worth reading, no slideshow worth watching and no music worth listening to ever came alive without some sort of outline. And if the plot of a simple two-hour movie requires preplanning, the distillation of your entire life certainly does. The plan can be in your head or it can consist of elaborate Roman-enumerated headings, but there has to be one or the result will likely be a "yada yada yada nugget yada yada yada" Ethical Will and not very effective in communicating your message. A little later I talk about simple ways to create an outline for your journey in creativity.

🎬11-9 The second part of crafting an effective Ethical Will is making sure that your audience hears *you* when they share your Ethical Will. Answering the following questions will narrow your message and help you find what makes your message unique. You'll be halfway there:

> *Why am I creating an Ethical Will?*

> *Who will be sharing my Ethical Will?*

The goal of finding *your* voice is very simple: to make certain that your Ethical Will sounds like *you*.

🎬11-10 So, the stage is set: paper, pen, blank computer screen, thesaurus, soothing music, the lighting is just right. Nothing is happening.

🎬11-11 That's because the tools of writing are not the same as the seeds of creativity. Inspiration and creativity start with a picture inside your head. It may be a vision of you reading a letter to your family or of everyone watching a slideshow at your wedding anniversary or it may be your loved ones gathered, smiling as they watch the video you left for them. May I remind you that many—really, most—of the ideas contained in *Chapters Seven* through *Ten* suggest Ethical Wills that can sound like you even if you don't create an original message from scratch.

Remember, your life is the story wrapped around your message but your Ethical Will *is* the message, the Cliff Notes® of your life. If you're not confident in your ability to *write* your message, try *telling* your message. 🎬11-12 Look out at your imaginary audience and tell the tale that is woven through your outline. Really listen to yourself while you are speaking. Then write down what you just said. Take it from there. 🎬11-13 Even James Michener said, *"I'm not a very good writer, but I'm an excellent re-writer."*

I think we both agree that you would rather skip the years of suffering for your art before you produce a decent Ethical Will. Nothing can exist until it is first imagined, so start by visualizing what you want the end product to look like, of course subject to re-writing and modifying and changing your mind. Here are some methods to jog your memory, to get your ideas in order and to get your message on the right track.

🎬11-14 **Photographs**

🎬11-15 If ever a commercial could bring one to tears, it was Kodak's 1970s montage with Paul Anka singing *The Times of Your Life.*[108] That's because pictures invite memories of places and faces and feelings. Dig out those boxes of pictures that you've been meaning to catalog and put into albums and sort them a bit. You may find that looking at some of the people and times of your life will inspire thoughts on the core message of your Ethical Will. How did those people affect your values, teach you or help to build your dreams? Look at your young self: how have your beliefs grown and changed, what has life taught you, what do you hope it will teach to your loved ones? (An unexpected bonus: the photos get organized!)

11-16 The times of your life

11-17 While you're looking at those old photos, set aside the ones that commemorate special times: a birthday, a wedding, a reunion, a baptism, a retirement, a new home, a memorable vacation or a family holiday. Think about the people pictured. Perhaps those scenes will focus your thinking on what each occasion meant to you, how it has influenced your values since then, what you wish you had said to those pictured or the dreams that were fashioned or fulfilled on that day.

11-18 World events

11-19 *"Where were you when...?"* Looking back on the events that shaped history during your lifetime not only reminds you where you were and what you were thinking but also makes you recognize how world events have shaped your personal history. Were your beliefs and values transformed that day? What life lessons did you learn from what happened? How did each historical event change your hopes and dreams going forward? Were you ever the same afterwards?

11-20 Local interest

One of the many things I love about the internet is the access to seemingly endless sources of information. I once Googled "vintage photos buses Des Moines Iowa" for use in a PowerPoint presentation and got more than 19,000 "hits." 11-21 Yikes—who were all those people taking pictures of buses in the 1950s? Try the same for your hometown to discover images of key events and places that were part of your childhood. Memories of landmarks and activities that no longer exist can be like getting a whiff of a long-forgotten aroma: you are transported. And being there in your mind and imagination is an opportunity to think about how those times and places molded your beliefs, taught you lessons and influenced your dreams.

11-22 **Life's background music**

Like the smell of familiar cologne or cuisine, a song can take us to a time and place in the past, most especially if it is the same recording we once knew. 11-23 Visit your collection of records, cassette tapes and CDs and dust off the ones you have not heard since shortly after purchasing them with your hard-earned allowance or dancing to them at your wedding. Again, there are a gajillion websites to access Top 40 record charts from any decade and even more sites available to listen to and/or download your favorites in case your mom sold yours at a garage sale.[109] Satellite radio is also a great option for listening to any and all genres of music.

11-24 Vintage television theme songs have the power to transport me to another time, another place. In the early days of network broadcasting, shows were not moved about the schedule as they are now. Remembering a show also means recalling the time, the day of the week and what you experienced just before and after the show. After school was *Where the Action Is*, Saturday mornings meant *Looney Tunes*, Saturday night was *Alfred Hitchcock Presents* and Sunday night was *The Wonderful World of Disney* and *The Ed Sullivan Show* (for special episodes, a TV tray in front of the only television in the house). Close your eyes and remember where you were when you first heard that theme song or watched that show. What stage of life were you experiencing back then? What have you learned since? Have the hopes and dreams you had then come true? What wisdom can you share with your loved ones to help them fulfill their own destinies?

11-25 **The roadmap of your life**

One day I got a wild hair to make a list of all the places I have lived in my life. Between college and our tendency to move, renovate, repeat, the list was freakishly long. I never did that again. 11-26 As for my childhood, it was spent entirely in one house on one unforgettable street: 57th Street Place, Des Moines, Iowa. And although there is a bounty and variety of memories, they always star the same actors and the same backdrop.

If you, on the other hand, are from a military family or someone whose mom or dad had a career requiring you to "move on to move up," consider using those varied locations and experiences as an outline for your Ethical Will. How were your beliefs and values affected by different cultures and communities? What did you learn about the meaning of "home" and "neighborhood" from your experiences? Who are the special people who passed through your life? Are your nomadic experiences reflected in your hopes for your loved ones? Did that lifestyle give you the wanderlust or render you a die-hard homebody?

✎11-27 Life's treasures

A little earlier in *Chapter Two*, I spoke of using your Ethical Will to direct gift giving during your life and bequests after you are gone. The treasures, the things that have deep sentimental value to you, can guide the message of your Ethical Will as well.

✎11-28 Look at each item and focus on who first owned it, how it came to you, where and how old you were when you received it, how its original owner shaped your beliefs, what you learned from him or her and how the treasure and its donor may have shaped your hopes and dreams. I am the custodian of a beautiful 1946 dollhouse, given to me when its original owner, my cousin Mary Kathryn, moved on to more sophisticated interests. I played with it throughout my childhood and continue to gaze at it lovingly. It was key to my obsession with all things miniature, and from it grew my fondness of decorating and making a nurturing home. It has been a treasure throughout my life and fortunate is the one who inherits it and all it represents from me.

✎11-29 The serial project

If the thought of sitting down to compose an Ethical Will is just too daunting to approach, consider a progressive version, with bits contributed over time. ✎11-30 Your Ethical Will: The Series.

Every year there is a class picture or a school photo, a pictorial of growth and change. How awesome would it be—for the parent and the child—to look back on these photos and find a note attached to each, reflecting a parent's ethical message? It can be a way to follow your life or that of a child or grandchild. You can reflect on the beliefs, lessons and hopes of your past year or your observations of theirs. And sometime between kindergarten and high school graduation, the child in those pictures is capable of noting his or her own thoughts on life, what the past grade has meant and hopes for the coming school year.

🎬11-31

Is that a group of hopeful faces, or what? And rightfully so. We were young and full of hope—and beans. I was thinking that if a note had accompanied each of my class pictures, what a wonderful record it would be, to look back on the essence of my growing self.[110]

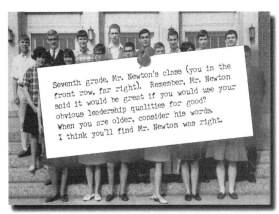

On the heels of the *April Fool's Day Massacre* in which we turned Mr. Newton's desk drawers upside down, the note accompanying this picture should have read something like this:

Seventh grade, Mr. Newton's class (you in the
front row, far right). Remember, Mr. Newton
said it would be great if you would use your
obvious leadership qualities for good?
When you are older, consider his words.
I think you'll find Mr. Newton was right.

🎬11-32 If your family has an annual portrait taken or sends out a holiday letter, either one is an apt opportunity to reflect on the past year and what it has meant in the evolution of your beliefs and values, life lessons or hopes for the future.[111]

∽ Christmas 2009 ∾
While we try to teach our children all about life,
Our children teach us what life is all about.

Consider including that message as a gift to the recipients of your newsletter or just add a simple note each year and collect them in a safe place. You could even look back now on past years to reflect and record—I'm betting that memories will flood back and you will find inspiration and meaning in those faces and letters. Even better if you are one of those holiday letter writers (personally, I love to get those braggy epistles each year—anything to stay in touch) for recalling the milestones of your life.

⌐11-33 A progressive Ethical Will can be a series of letters addressed to loved ones, one written every year on your birthday, your anniversary or New Year's Day. Remember and emulate the tradition that the late Rabbi Richard Israel established and practiced: a special message given to children as they reach milestones in their own lives.[112] Remember the best way to eat an elephant: in many small bites.

⌐11-34 A simple outline for an Ethical Will

⌐11-35 - ⌐11-37 Revisit the first page of this chapter to review the basics of an Ethical Will. That summary can also serve as a simple outline for your creativity. Read each paragraph, then write down the values, lessons or hopes that first pop into your head. It's a start that quickly shows that yes, you have an Ethical Will in you, yearning to breathe free.

In preparing to create your Ethical Will, consider the answers to these questions: ⌐11-38

Why are you writing it? Is it a stand-alone document or will it be used to supplement charitable gift, end-of-life or estate planning?
Who is your audience? Who will be sharing it?

🎬11-39
What medium would you like to use for your completed version?
Because it may affect the format and the message, when do you plan to share your Ethical Will?
Do you have a deadline or goal for finishing? If not, set one now to stay on track.

_____
_____
_____
_____
_____
_____
_____
_____
_____
_____
_____

🎬11-40 A prompting outline

🎬11-41 I'll take a multiple-choice exam over an essay test anytime. Maybe you feel the same. In case none of these suggestions for getting started has appealed to you, *Chapter Twelve* contains my *Desiderata* template for creating an Ethical Will. It's a no-fail approach that focuses your thinking, no matter what type of medium you have pictured in your mind for the final product.

🎬11-42 *Above all, because an Ethical Will is your opportunity to leave a unique message of affection, inspiration and hope for your loved ones, there is no right or wrong way to express your thoughts. It's okay to make 'em laugh. It's okay to make 'em cry. The important thing is to share your message with sounds and sights that leave no doubt as to the creator—you.*

End of Chapter Eleven
🎬11-43

Review - Chapter Eleven

- No matter what form it takes, the basic elements of an Ethical Will are beliefs and values, life lessons and hopes for the future.
- An effective Ethical Will should follow an outline, to make sure that key messages are effectively communicated.
- Ask yourself: *Why am I creating an Ethical Will?* and *Who will be sharing my Ethical Will?*
- To assist in organizing your thoughts, try using one of these to guide your outline: vintage or family photographs, a timeline of the special occasions and events of your life, historical world events, memories of your hometown, familiar music from your life story, the map of where you have lived or treasured heirlooms.
- A serial Ethical Will can be created by adding your ethical message to a class picture or annual holiday photo or letter.

- A simple outline for your Ethical Will can be prepared by considering the answers to these questions:

  Why are you writing it? Is it a stand-alone document or will it be used to supplement charitable gift, end-of-life or estate planning?

  Who is your audience? Who will be sharing it?

  What medium would you like to use for your completed version?

  Because it may affect the format and the message, when do you plan to share your Ethical Will?

  Do you have a deadline or goal for finishing? If not, set one now to stay on track.

- A prompting outline can serve as the basis for a more extensive Ethical Will, for an audio or video version or as a stand-alone ethical message.

Ponder this...
Questions for discussion

1. When it comes to creating your Ethical Will, which word best describes you: **excited** or **anxious**? Why? _____

   _____

2. If you have thought about why you are creating your Ethical Will here and now, please share that.

   _____

   _____

3. Does your decision to create an Ethical Will at this time in your life have any influence on the outline or key messages of your Ethical Will? If so, please share.

   _____

   _____

   _____

4. Have you decided what medium you will use to express your Ethical Will? If so, what influenced your decision and how will the format affect the "outline" that will guide the message of your Ethical Will?

   _____

   _____

   _____

5. Can you think of any serial event or record in your life that you could now revisit, adding the story of the values, lessons and hopes that are illustrated there?

   _____

   _____

   _____

   _____

   _____

   _____

   _____

Now, let's exercise our creativity...
Chapter Eleven - Exercise 1

Look at the photos of these three historical events. Choose one that you personally remember and write 100 words on how that event effected your values, life lessons or hopes for the future. Include your observations on when you realized the impact it had made on you. **(suggested: 5 minutes/100 words)**

November 22, 1963

September 25, 1981

September 11, 2001

_____
_____
_____
_____
_____
_____
_____
_____
_____
_____
_____
_____
_____
_____
_____
_____
_____
_____
_____
_____
_____

Chapter Eleven - Exercise 2

Choose a valued family heirloom that you received from a beloved ancestor or friend. Write 100 words to accompany the bequest of that treasure when you pass it on to another. Focus on the values that accompanied that treasure when it came to you and will travel along to its next caretaker. **(suggested: 10 minutes/100 words)**

Fill your paper with the breathings of your heart.
William Wordsworth

ဆာ **Notes to Self** ကန

And though I have not understood all this,
Made up of a laugh and a wail;
I think that the God of the world knows all,
And some day will tell the tale.
Max Ehrmann[113]
🎬12-1

🎬12-2 ဆ Chapter Twelve ର
The guidance of *Desiderata*

Notes to Self

🎬12-3 The poem *Desiderata*[114] endured a remarkable odyssey to reach me and come to rest in the pages of this book. It started in 1927 as the work of 🎬12-4 Max Ehrmann, a lawyer-turned-poet from Terra Haute, Indiana. He shared *Desiderata* with his friend, Dr. Merrill Moore, who gave out more than 1,000 copies to patients and continued to do so while serving as a World War II Army psychiatrist. From that time on, *Desiderata* was missing any notice of the federal copyright that Max Ehrmann had obtained when he wrote it. 🎬12-5 The Reverend Frederick W. Kates, rector of Old Saint Paul's Church in Baltimore, included the poem in a book he published in 1957, again without credit to Ehrmann, and handed out more copies of the poem to members of his congregation in the late 1950s.[115]

Widely distributed on the letterhead of Old Saint Paul's Church in the 1960s, many mistook the date that the parish was founded—1692—for the year the poem was composed by an "anonymous author." The urban legend spread and the supposed ancient poem was said to have been inexplicably discovered in the church.[116] When American politician 🎬12-6 Adlai Stevenson passed away in 1965, *Desiderata*'s notoriety was renewed when it was found among his papers; he had planned to enclose it with his Christmas cards later that year.[117] Moving right along with the times, *Desiderata* became a 1971 hit record in the United States and Great Britain, earning a Grammy award for *Best Spoken Word Recording* by Les Crane, a radio and television talk-show host.[118]

🎬12-7 Meanwhile, the widow of Max Ehrmann bequeathed the publishing rights to a nephew upon her death in 1965, who then sold the copyright to Robert L. Bell in 1967, or so Mr. Bell believed.[119] The U.S. Court of Appeals did not agree. In 1976 it ruled that the copyright to *Desiderata* had been forfeited by Max Ehrmann when he allowed its distribution by Dr. Moore in 1942 and 1944 without requiring any compensation or maintenance of the copyright notice. Robert L. Bell had acquired zilch and *Desiderata* is now officially in the public domain.[120]

☙12-8 In *Desiderata*, Max Ehrmann shared timeless wisdom on values, life lessons and hopes—his philosophy of life—that has inspired countless readers for more than eight decades. It is ironic and somehow fitting that the same man who unknowingly surrendered the exclusive rights to *Desiderata* in 1942 had penned these words in 1927:   ☙12-9

> *Exercise caution in your business affairs;*
> *for the world is full of trickery.*
> *But let this not blind you to what virtue there is;*
> *many persons strive for high ideals;*
> *and everywhere life is full of heroism.*

Max Ehrmann
September 26, 1872 – September 9, 1945

☙12-10 But wait! We're not quite to the end of *Desiderata's* journey. A dear friend, now passed, shared with me a copy of *Desiderata* the morning after my first husband, Roy Z. Fort, died suddenly. I have kept it since then, a prized possession that I no longer noticed because it had become such an element of my personal landscape. I reread it not long ago and smiled to realize that *Desiderata* is an extraordinary example of an Ethical Will.

So, I share it with you as a time-travelling guide to creating your Ethical Will. ☙12-11 Like any all-encompassing Ethical Will would, its stanzas cover the subjects of *communication, self-esteem, work, love, health, self-awareness and spirituality.*

☙12-12 Prompting thoughts or questions focus your thinking and narrow the message as you create your Ethical Will. As you read through the questions I have written to accompany each stanza, answer those that interest you and/or apply—skip the rest. ☙12-13 Use as much space as you need—you may want to compose this Ethical Will with word processing software to allow plenty of artistic license. Lengthy prose is not objectionable as long as you remain focused on the core elements of your Ethical Will. So please do try to stay on message.

Then string your answers together to make the outline of your slideshow, audio recording, embellished album or scrapbook, video production or simple handwritten letter. ☛12-14 You may also choose to simply add a "Dear loved ones" at the beginning of *Desiderata* and sign your name at the end. ☛12-15 If Max Ehrmann, this extraordinary attorney-turned-poet, found the enduring inspiration to say all the things you wish you had said, why not?

You are a child of the universe,
no less than the trees and the stars;
you have a right to be here.
Max Ehrmann
☛12-16

ᔆᓄ Notes to Self ᐤᔕ

🎬12-17

ℰ᧐ **Desiderata** ᢕᎯ
by Max Ehrmann

I. Communication, creativity, education, speech, the spoken and written word, talking, listening

Go placidly amid the noise and haste,
and remember what peace there may be in silence.
As far as possible without surrender
be on good terms with all persons.
Speak your truth quietly and clearly;
and listen to others, even the dull and the ignorant;
they too have their story.

🎬12-18

The most effective way to express oneself is to

_____

The most important lesson I learned from someone else is

_____

The importance of lifelong learning is

_____

My best memories of formal education are

_____

The most influential book I ever read is

_____

The most influential movie I ever saw is

_____

I had a special teacher who made a difference in my life by

_____

I think the role of education in one's life is to

_____

My advice to others is

_____

In writing this Ethical Will, I learned something about myself that I didn't know before

_____

_____

II. Self-esteem, achievement, power, will, inner decisions about life, assertiveness

Avoid loud and aggressive persons,
they are vexations to the spirit.
If you compare yourself with others,
you may become vain and bitter;
for always there will be greater
and lesser persons than yourself.
Enjoy your achievements as well as your plans.
12-19

I have come to define "success" as

_____

_____

The achievements I am most proud of are

_____

_____

I believe that real "power" means to

_____

_____

I made a difference by

_____

_____

The most memorable dream I had as I was growing up is

_____

_____

The unfulfilled dream I most regret is

_____

_____

When I am gone, I'd like others to describe me as

_____

_____

_____

_____

_____

_____

_____

_____

_____

_____

_____

III. Work, integrity, reputation, compassion, emotions, love, forgiveness

Keep interested in your own career, however humble;
it is a real possession in the changing fortunes of time.
Exercise caution in your business affairs;
for the world is full of trickery.
But let this not blind you to what virtue there is;
many persons strive for high ideals;
and everywhere life is full of heroism.

📽12-20

I pursued my profession because

_____

_____

The part of my career that was most fulfilling to me was

_____

_____

The person who most influenced my professional life and success is

_____

_____

The best job I ever had was when I

_____

_____

The business principle most essential to my success is

_____

_____

The greatest hero of my life is

_____

_____

The values I would never compromise are

_____

_____

I am proud of standing up for my beliefs when I

_____

_____

The best way to measure professional success is by

_____

_____

The role of money in my life is to

_____

_____

My financial philosophy is

_____

_____

IV. Love, family, friendship, relationships, emotions, desires, feelings, procreation

Be yourself.
Especially, do not feign affection.
Neither be cynical about love;
for in the face of all aridity and disenchantment
it is as perennial as the grass.
📖12-21

The most important part of being a family is

_____

_____

The ethnic history of my family influenced my life in the following ways

_____

_____

The saying or expression that best expresses our family is

_____

_____

The earliest memory I have as a child is

_____

_____

My favorite family story is

_____

_____

To me, the love of my family means

_____

_____

The ancestor I remember best is

_____

_____

His or her greatest influence on me is

_____

_____

The values I hold which came from my ancestors are

_____

_____

The thing that I learned from my parents or grandparents that holds meaning for me is

_____

_____

From the children in my life, I learned

_____

_____

When I think of a best friend, I think of

_____

_____

Some of the special people in my life are

_____

_____

The people I consider mentors or guides in my life are

_____

_____

The person who brought out the very best in me is

_____

_____

For my immediate loved ones, I hope that the future brings

_____

_____

More than anything else, I want my family to

_____

_____

My most beloved pets are/were

_____

_____

From the animals in my life, I learned

_____

_____

_____

_____

_____

_____

_____

_____

_____

_____

_____

_____

_____

_____

_____

_____

V. Physical, emotional and spiritual health, physical needs, security

Take kindly the counsel of the years,
gracefully surrendering the things of youth.
Nurture strength of spirit to shield you
in sudden misfortune.
But do not distress yourself with dark imaginings.
Many fears are born of fatigue and loneliness.
Beyond a wholesome discipline, be gentle with yourself.
12-22

The favorite memory I have of growing up is

_____

_____

My attitude about growing older is most influenced by

_____

_____

The person who I consider my role model for graceful aging is

_____

_____

My advice for having good health and a long life is to

_____

_____

I found the best way to overcome disappointment in life is to

_____

_____

To me, "aging" means to

_____

_____

The best way I know to stay young in mind and body is to

_____

_____

When I feel weak or drained of spirit, my method of renewal is

_____

_____

I have to admit, I wish I had done more

_____

_____

_____

_____

_____

_____

_____

VI. Self-awareness, intuition, insight, spiritual power, reasoning, seeing/intuiting

You are a child of the universe,
no less than the trees and the stars;
you have a right to be here.
And whether or not it is clear to you,
no doubt the universe is unfolding as it should.
12-23

I believe my purpose in life is to

_____

_____

My favorite way to get and stay in touch with my feelings is to

_____

_____

I have learned that the best means for me to grow spiritually is to

_____

_____

My most important "life changing" event was when

_____

_____

The most fun I ever had was when I

_____

_____

The greatest blessing in my life is

_____

_____

My hope for a better world is that

_____

_____

I am most grateful for

_____

_____

When I am gone, I would like people to remember the following three things about me

_____

_____

_____

_____

_____

VII. Spirituality, wisdom,
being one with the world, divinity, a higher power

Therefore be at peace with God,
whatever you conceive Him to be,
and whatever your labors and aspirations,
in the noisy confusion of life keep peace with your soul.
🎬12-24

The importance of religion in my family and personal life is evidenced by

_____

_____

I would describe my perception of my higher power as

_____

_____

I most felt the presence of my higher power when

_____

_____

I believe that after I pass from this life on Earth, I will

_____

_____

The thing I am most thankful for in my life is

_____

_____

As I look back at my life, the historical event I lived through that influenced me the most was

_____

_____

When that happened, I remember exactly where I was

_____

_____

I hope that the world of the future will include

_____

_____

My philosophy of life in a short phrase is

_____

If I had my life to live over, I would

_____

_____

My contribution to the betterment of society is

_____

_____

_____

With all its sham, drudgery, and broken dreams,
it is still a beautiful world.
Be cheerful.
Strive to be happy.
🎬12-25

My favorite quotation is
_____

_____

My favorite song is
_____

My favorite poem is
_____

My favorite book or prose is
_____

My favorite movie is
_____

Charities that most clearly exemplify my feelings and beliefs about giving and mission are
_____

_____

_____

The qualities that these charities display and foster are
_____

_____

_____

I have made a list of treasured possessions to be passed on when I am gone. Please read that list to understand why I made those gifts to the special people in my life.

End of Chapter Twelve
🎬12-26

Ponder this...

After hearing the story of Max Ehrmann's *Desiderata*, consider the countless lives of those who have read it, cherished it, even tried to live its message over the eight decades of its journey. Before beginning the process of creating your own Ethical Will, reflect on your potential to shape the values of others. Assume that those who are blessed to share your ethical message will cherish it and will even try to emulate the values you express in it. Nothing can exist until it is first imagined...

Now, let's exercise our creativity...

If you want to continue to hone your writing skills, complete one or more of the exercises following here. An added benefit: any one may lead you to more memories, life lessons and hopes to share with your loved ones. I agree: the more you write, the better you write.

Chapter Twelve - Exercise 1

Pack a "value survival kit": the beliefs and values you hold that you could not live without. Look at the list on Page 133 in the *Appendix* and choose 1-3 descriptive words from it. Then write for 10 minutes on why you believe each is vital to the survival of your ethical self.

Chapter Twelve - Exercise 2

Do you have a collection of any kind? If so, write 150 words on why the objects appeal to you. Is it a reflection in any way of your values, life lessons or hopes for the future? Do you remember how and when you started collecting?

Chapter Twelve - Exercise 3

Write about a family tradition that you experienced in childhood (holidays, birthdays, vacations, seasonal events). Does it illustrate one or more values that your family holds? If so, write 150 words about that custom, what it meant to you as a child and how it has influenced the family traditions you are establishing or practicing as an adult.

Chapter Twelve - Exercise 4

Did you move often as a child? If so, write 150 words on how that has affected your definition of "home" and how it has influenced your relationships with family and friends.

Chapter Twelve - Exercise 5

Gratitude. What are you most thankful for in your life right now? Write for 10 minutes on that and how your answer might have been different—if you think it would have been—ten years ago today.

Chapter Twelve - Exercise 6

What is your best talent? Is it exhibited at your job, in your hobby, as a friend, spouse or parent? Write for 10 minutes on what makes you exceptional in that role. Focus on which of your core values helps you to excel.

Chapter Twelve - Exercise 7

What memories do these pictures evoke? Study them for a few moments and choose the one from your own "growing up" decade. When it comes to family and societal values, do you think life back then was really different or is it just our perceptions that have changed? What about your personal values—have they changed since then? Free-write (just jot down your reflections as they come) for 15 minutes. Then review your thoughts—is there a theme?

The 1950s

The 1970s

The 1990s

The greatest use of life is to spend it
for something that will outlast it.
William James

❧ Notes to Self ☙

An invisible red thread connects those who are destined to meet,
regardless of time, place or circumstance.
The thread may stretch or tangle, but it will never break.
Ancient Chinese Proverb
◖E-1

ℬ Epilogue ℭ
◖E-2

◖E-3 Now that you know as much as I know about Ethical Wills, this book may not seem to qualify as one, but from where I'm sitting, the process of remembering, learning anew and writing about the people, places and events of my life has been both reflective and inspiring. As I reviewed my life and the extraordinary people who have meandered through it, I personified a therapist's diagnostic checklist: sad, mad, bad, glad. Not unlike most people, life for me has been a mosaic of mind-numbing losses and seemingly undeserved, always unexpected and incredibly marvelous blessings. But right here, right now, it's all good.

I was pretty cocky when I started writing this book. I was going to teach you how to hone a message of your beliefs and values, life lessons and hopes for the future. I was uniquely qualified because I did my homework on Ethical Wills and—hey!—I knew exactly what I stood for. Turns out I didn't. But I do now, at least for today.

Every decisive episode in my life contained an essential lesson for me although, admittedly, it took me many years to appreciate the teachable moments in some. But that is the spirit of an Ethical Will: ultimately recognizing the lessons in everyday life and using that wisdom to benefit yourself and others. And that's how I would like to be remembered: as a learner and a teacher.

Please give yourself the gift of time: time to reflect on what you believe, what you know and what you hope for and time to share your hard-earned wisdom with your loved ones. It's a journey well worth taking. Time is so precious. Thank you for sharing some of yours with me.

◖E-4 March 1, 2011 Postscript to the Epilogue

I came late to being a writer. It was a dream that I ignored. I failed to give it the respect it deserved in my life because others did not and that was wrong of me. I hope this *Workshop Edition of SO GROWS THE TREE* gives you the means and courage to be the person you are meant to be: someone who expresses ideas and shares wisdom and--going forward--learns from the past, lives for today and hopes for the future. ◖E-5

The end of the beginning...

A bird doesn't sing because it has an answer,
It sings because it has a song.
Maya Angelou

Words that come from the heart enter the heart.
Hebrew proverb

ᏸ **Notes to Self** ᏸ

*The invariable mark of wisdom is to see
the miraculous in the common.*
Ralph Waldo Emerson

ॐ Appendix ॐ

ॐ A few well-chosen words ॐ

In *Chapter Eight*, I wrote of using a list of words to inspire your writing and here it is. Use these terms to create unique prose, read them as prompts and inspiration for an Ethical Will or string them together with examples and anecdotes and compose a personal essay.

acceptance accountability accomplishment achievement affection allegiance assertiveness balance bravery caring character class comfort commitment communication compassion concern confidence convictions courage creativity credo decisiveness dependability determination dignity diligence discipline education equality empathy example excellence fairness faith family flexibility forgiveness friendship generosity gratitude guidance hard work help honesty honor humility humor inner peace integrity intelligence inventiveness justice kindness learning leadership legacy loyalty love mindfulness modesty moral compass morality optimism passion patience perception perseverance persistence personal growth positive attitude power pride quality reason reliability reputation resolve respect responsibility risk-taking selflessness self-esteem self-reflection self-respect sensitivity spirit spirituality strength style survival sympathy teamwork thoughtfulness trust trustworthiness truthfulness understanding warmth wisdom

The difference between the right word
and the almost right word
is the difference between lightning and a lightning bug.
Mark Twain

℘ Notes to Self ℀

*Memories are like sand castles - only by putting them
in a safe place can you prevent them from washing away.*
Anonymous

๛ Safeguarding your Ethical Will ๛

You will want to share and perhaps even display your Ethical Will when completed. This chapter is a vital part of the creating and sharing process: *preserving* your Ethical Will. Your Ethical Will will be part of your legacy, a gift that will survive you to be passed on to your descendants. When that time comes, let's make sure your well-crafted message is still there to share.

Time is Enemy Number One when it comes to conserving heirlooms. The elements that surround us on a daily basis are not harmful taken one moment at a time, but when allowed to work their chemical magic over years or even decades, light, moisture, bugs, mold/mildew and pollution are demons to our valuable documents. The principal bad boys are light (natural or fluorescent) and humidity, but one little mouse (or book lice—ick) can decimate the family bible in an innocent quest for the perfect nesting material. In the category of sudden disasters, the threats of fire, theft, tornado, hurricane and flood also hover. It doesn't matter how far you are from the nearest body of water if your family scrapbook is in a box next to the washing machine and it blows a hose. Water is water and it always seeks its own level.

If you don't believe that environment can damage, just visit the Star Spangled Banner at the Smithsonian. It now lies in state, cloistered in a light- and climate-controlled laboratory, conserved after being openly displayed in various national museums for over 80 years. It is minus the 200 square feet of fabric that was snipped away as souvenirs before the Armistead family gifted it to the nation in 1912.[121] What could we have been thinking? Well, we were thinking that it was important for our citizenry to view, perhaps even touch, this historic relic. Sadly, the cost of that worthy goal was the integrity of its priceless fabric. It's a valuable lesson to remember when you start to think about the future generations that you hope will share your Ethical Will by seeing, hearing or even holding it.

To the list of natural disasters add the contemporary genre of computer viruses and crashes. Who are those angry people in jammies who spend their lonely existence thinking of ways to destroy other people's hard drives? Never mind, just take steps to have a backup plan so that if and when disaster of any kind strikes, you only lose one of multiple copies.

Notes to Self

Copying your Ethical Will

Depending on the type of Ethical Will you create and when you plan to share it with others, you may want to distribute copies to many persons or you may be putting it in the "Open upon my death" envelope. In either case, you need a means to duplicate and safely store your Ethical Will and backup copies.

A digital record is a file on a computer hard drive, CD, DVD, flashdrive or memory card. Once an Ethical Will is converted to digital format, every type (okay, except for a memory jug or quilt) can be easily duplicated and safely stored for preservation. A scanner is much like a copier, except that when you lay the document on the image glass, it converts the document or picture to a digital file on an attached computer hard drive. Although today's home scanner is both affordable and user-friendly, if you don't have one and don't want to have one, commercial printers are equipped and eager to scan your documents at a reasonable cost and to provide a digitized record in the format of your choice. (If you use a commercial printer, make sure it is a professional who appreciates the significance of the phrase "priceless, irreplaceable original.")

If you are scanning or copying original documents or photographs yourself, be very careful. *Never* put an irreplaceable document or photograph through a feeder—always lay it flat on the image glass of the copier or scanner. Anytime you copy an original for preservation, copy it onto archival paper.[122]

Handwritten documents

For any handwritten Ethical Will, whether a letter, an essay or a journal, scanning the document will allow you to store it as a digital record and to make multiple copies, for distribution now or in the future.

Computer-generated Ethical Wills

If your Ethical Will was created on a computer, you can skip the scanning step. When copying the file containing a letter, journal, digiscrapbook, digital photo album, embellished cookbook or PowerPoint slideshow, make sure any hard (paper) copies are printed onto archival paper and properly stored. For color images (a digi-scrapbook, photo album or slideshow), paper made specifically for photo printing is preferable to copier bond for product quality and preservation.

Three-dimensional Ethical Wills

If your Ethical Will is a traditional photo album, scrapbook or cookbook, first, congratulations! As much as I appreciate the computer and its almost endless options for creativity, there is nothing quite like turning the pages of a big old album to reveal the one-of-a-kind treasures on the next page. In assembling items for a scrapbook or photo album, consider using reproductions of scanned photographs, memorabilia or recipe cards, and putting the heirloom originals in storage. Ask the experts at your local scrapbooking store for assistance on using archival materials to assemble your book.[123]

Once completed, I recommend taking the book to a document scanning service. Just search "large format printing and scanning" online or in your local phone book. Once scanned, you will be able to print smaller scale copies or have the printer make a full-scale copy for every one of your lucky loved ones. How cool would it be to have a copy of your embellished family cookbook for each attendee at your next reunion!

Video and Audio Ethical Wills

The contemporary video camera is designed to upload its recordings to a computer, directly or by using a memory card, for editing and permanent storage. If your camera is not capable of this, take the video to a conversion service and have it digitized, so you can access it on your computer. This will also make it accessible for editing (rearranging segments, adding titles, adjusting volume).

Audio recordings can be easily made on your computer with the addition of an inexpensive microphone. If you are using an external tape recorder, use software such as *Audacity* to convert that recording into a digital file or take your tape to a media conversion service and have it put it into a digital format for editing and archiving.

Archiving your Ethical Will

Who knew that the 8-track and floppy disc would be such short-lived media? It begs the question: how long will the digital devices you are now using be around? How long will the data be intact and how long will you have the hardware necessary to access it?

The records on your computer will be there as long as the computer is functioning and the hard drive is accessible. However, if anything damages the computer, whether a natural disaster, a computer virus or a spilled cup of coffee, the files may be damaged or permanently lost. To eliminate the potential danger of these risks, once your valuable family papers and Ethical Will are digitized, immediately choose a backup method of storage.[124]

Compact Disc (CD) or Digital Video Disc (DVD)

Your first inclination may be to "just make lots of copies" of your CDs and DVDs and that is certainly an option, but not a long-term solution. CDs or DVDs that we make or "burn" on our home computers are not the same quality as the ones we buy at the music or video store. Home versions have a limited life, although we aren't sure how long that is. According to PC World magazine, "The jury is still out on whether the discs will last for years or decades." [125] We do know that CDs and DVDs which are "rewritable" (CD-RWs and DVD-RWs) definitely have a shorter life than CD-Rs and DVD-Rs.[126] And if you think 100 years is plenty long for preservation, how old are those personal papers of Great-grandfather's that you so lovingly cherish?

Backup systems

A backup system is a method of copying the files on your computer to a second storage medium. Yes, I know you already have a formal backup system, but this discussion is about actually using it.

Off-site storage. You can schedule regular remote backups into an internet library via the Web. Ponder this: the system is as reliable and secure as the company providing. I'm just saying...

External drive. This is a second hard drive used to hold records originated on your main computer, either by transferring files out of your main hard drive or duplicating them on an external drive. A backup hard drive is still subject to natural and computer disasters but will not be affected by injury to your main computer.

Memory card or flash card. How does all that information fit onto a teeny, tiny piece of plastic? These portable devices are easily inserted into your computer to upload or download digital files. They are not recommended for archival storage, however, due to their indeterminate life span. Frankly, many of these media have not been around long enough to be tested, longevity-wise. But we do know that memory cards can be corrupted, so that makes them unreliable as a long-term archival solution.

Flash drive. Also known as a memory stick, key drive, pen drive and jump drive, a flash drive looks like a very thin cigarette lighter with a USB plug on the end. Flash drives are available in one to 64 Gigabyte sizes, plenty ginormous to hold anything you can produce, including slides, graphics and photographs. Easy to transport and store, flash drives have a virtually unlimited lifespan and their contents can be uploaded to any computer for printing or re-archiving in another format. You can also prepare and give a flash drive of important documents to each loved ones at a reasonable cost.

Sharing your Ethical Will

You know best the time that is most fitting to share your Ethical Will with the special people in your life. If that time is right after you finish it, you may want to distribute copies directly. If you are sharing long-distance, most computer files can be attached to an e-mail and shared as a document or even as an attached slideshow.

For the Ethical Will that is meant to be shared after you are gone, perhaps as part of your memorial service, be sure that the file with your Letter of Instructions is not *too* well stored. Do not put it in the safety deposit box—it may not be opened until weeks after your death. More appropriately, talk to the person who is your health care proxy or standby attorney-in-fact for financial matters and tell them where they can find the envelope that should be opened immediately upon your death. In it they will find your wishes for final disposition, a detailed funeral or memorial plan and a copy of your Ethical Will to be shared. Right?

Original heirloom documents

Having encouraged you to find and study your dusty photographs and family papers as a source of inspiration, I can hardly discuss preservation without including those priceless original documents. Just a reminder: in assembling items for a scrapbook or photo album, consider using reproductions of scanned photographs, memorabilia or recipe cards, and putting those heirloom originals in storage. It is beyond the scope of this book (and the author) to make you an expert archivist, but here are a few basic rules.

Photographs
High humidity is the enemy of all photographs and high temperature is the enemy of color prints. Handle photos carefully, wearing cotton gloves if necessary. Never keep photos in "magnetic" (self-sticking) photo albums; store them in acid-free boxes, folders or polyester sleeves. Please identify the people and places in photos, but do so by writing lightly on the back edge of the picture with a pencil or add a label to the outside of the sleeve. Framing of historic photographs should be done only by a professional, using archival backings, mats and light-filtering glass.[127]

Documents
All the advice above applies as well for documents such as birth, baptism, marriage and death certificates, but I would add

that you should use only acid-free folders, divider pages and boxes to store papers. Never fold documents. Always lay them flat and remove—very carefully—any paper clips, rubber bands and staples.[128] (Perhaps I should add "straight pins" to that list since I have found papers held together with them as well!) Plastic sleeves work well for storage, provided they are made of archival polyester. Be sure that storage is dry and dark, using boxes that are sturdy and acid- and pest-free.

For damaged documents, seek the services of a professional conservationist to restore and preserve the original. If you do suffer a disaster, immediate remedial steps can mitigate the damage[129]—but still call a professional.[130]

Media files

It's a bit mind-numbing, but VHS, 8-track and reel-to-reel tapes are quickly falling into an "heirloom" category all their own: media that can no longer be enjoyed because the players can only be found at the Smithsonian American History Museum and garage sales. Add computer floppy discs to that list.

Take old 8mm family movies to the nearest professional conversion service to be digitized for preservation. If you have an audio tape worth listening to, convert it to a computer file with easy-to-use software or have the professionals do so. Same with anything stored on a floppy disc: if you still want to retrieve the information, have it put onto a flashdrive or CD and transfer it onto a more permanent, accessible and portable medium as soon as possible.

An Ethical Will is a magnificent gift and ultimately a legacy for those who get to share it and for you, the creator. It can applaud as well as inspire, so consider sharing it while you are still here to see the grateful smiles. The sooner your wisdom helps others, the better!

But no matter when you choose to share your Ethical Will, take care to copy, preserve and store it so that it will be conserved and available in the future.

If your actions inspire others to dream more, learn more,
do more and become more, you are a leader.
John Quincy Adams

℘ The workshop facilitator's guide ℘

To quote William Shakespeare's observation on leaders: *"Some are born great, some achieve greatness and others have greatness thrust upon them."* The responsibility of the Ethical Will workshop facilitator is to organize the workshop and then sit back and accept the accolades. I hope that your willingness to read this chapter means you fit into one of The Bard's three categories.

Although duties are few, rewards are plentiful. You will be doing more than just facilitating a workshop; you will be key in helping many others leave their bequests of values, their Ethical Wills.

Checklist for conducting an Ethical Will workshop
✓ Have the desire to meet with others to learn about and create an Ethical Will. Mark this one done!
✓ Gauge the interest in others by sending a mass e-mail and/or snail mail or posting a flyer about the Ethical Will workshop coming soon (**EXHIBITS A** and **B**).
✓ When you know how many people have registered to attend the workshop, confirm the location. If response exceeds the planned space (what a great problem to have!), you can split into multiple workshop groups.
✓ Obtain a copy of *The Workshop Edition of SO GROWS THE TREE* for each attendee. I suggest you collect the cost as part of the registration process. Then you can order online at *www.SoGrowsTheTree.com* or *www.Amazon.com* or ask your local bookstore to place an order. Allow time for each registrant to receive his or her book at least a week before the first Slideshow Session.
✓ E-mail, snail mail or give each attendee the simple instructions for the first Workshop Session (**EXHIBIT C**).
✓ Workshop attendees may view the Slideshow Sessions on their own, together as part of the workshop schedule or you may offer group viewing sessions, prior to each Workshop Session. Whatever the case, let your attendees

Notes to Self
_____
_____
_____
_____
_____
_____
_____
_____
_____
_____
_____
_____
_____
_____
_____
_____
_____
_____
_____
_____
_____

know if, when and where those sessions will be held by inserting the information in **EXHIBIT C**.

✓ At each Workshop Session, read the announcement included here (**EXHIBIT D**). Then sit back and enjoy!

_____

_____

_____

Limited right to duplicate and distribute

These exhibits are provided exclusively for use by the purchaser of this book to organize and conduct a workshop using *The Workshop Edition of SO GROWS THE TREE*. This right does not extend to duplication and/or distribution of any other materials contained in The Workshop Edition of *SO GROWS THE TREE*. Thank you.

EXHIBIT A - Script of an e-mail or flyer to be sent to prospective Ethical Will workshop attendees:

Dear friend,

Have you ever heard of an Ethical Will?

Let me put it this way: *You know who got Grandma's pearls, but who got Grandma's pearls of wisdom?*

An Ethical Will is a message of your beliefs, life lessons and hopes for the future. Simply put, it's how you want to be remembered. Perhaps you've thought about leaving a legacy such as this, but you just didn't know how or where to begin. You are invited to be part of an Ethical Will workshop where you will learn about this ancient tradition and how to create and share your own legacy of values.

An Ethical Will can be expressed as a multimedia slideshow, a family cookbook, an embellished photo album, or a scrapbook journal. You can share a collection of favorite quotations or choose a poem that says it all for you. Or, it can be a simple letter addressed to your loved ones, typed or even handwritten.

The workshop will be three, two-hour sessions (either evenings or Saturday mornings) and the cost will be $_____ per person. Included in that fee is the workshop guide, *The Workshop Edition of SO GROWS THE TREE – Creating an Ethical Will* by Jo Kline Cebuhar, J.D. It has a narrated DVD that you can watch on your own or with others prior to each Workshop Session.

Please contact **[contact person]** at **[phone number or e-mail address]** to preregister or if you have questions about the workshop. If you would like to learn more about Ethical Wills and the book we will be using as our workshop guide, visit *www.SoGrowsTheTree.com*.

Hope you can join us!

[your name]

EXHIBIT B - Copy this flyer to distribute or to post:

You know who got Grandma's pearls, but who got Grandma's pearls of wisdom?

Would you like to learn about the ancient tradition of Ethical Wills and how to create your own legacy of beliefs, wisdom and hopes?

For more information about the upcoming

Ethical Will Workshop using

The Workshop Edition of

SO GROWS THE TREE

by Jo Kline Cebuhar, J.D.

please contact:

"Immortality is the genius to move others long after you have stopped moving."
Frank Rooney

EXHIBIT C - Script of an e-mail or note to be given to preregistered Ethical Will workshop attendees:

The Ethical Will Workshop will be held at
[location of the Workshop Sessions]
[include directions and parking info as needed]
on the following dates:

[dates of the three Workshop Sessions]
from _____ a.m. / p.m. to _____ a.m. / p.m.

If you have not already picked up your copy of *The Workshop Edition of SO GROWS THE TREE*, please do so before the first Workshop Session, read Pages v-42 in the book and watch the first Slideshow Session before the first Workshop Session. (See Page x in the book for a simple homework assignment.)
[If you are providing Slideshow Sessions as a group prior to Workshop Sessions, let the attendees know when and where they will be held.]

Please bring your own beverage and a snack to share during the break. We're looking forward to seeing you there!

Questions? Contact **[name and phone number or e-mail]**.

EXHIBIT D - Script of an announcement to be made at the beginning of each Workshop Session:

"Welcome and thank you for being a part of this Ethical Will workshop. We will take a break in the middle, but feel free to get up whenever you need to take a stretch.

I hope you've all had a chance to watch the Slideshow Session and read the chapters that we will cover in this Workshop Session. For each chapter in this Workshop Session, I'll ask for a volunteer to read the chapter Review, just to refresh our memories about what was covered.

I'll also ask for a volunteer to read each discussion question. There are no "right" or "wrong" answers to the discussion questions, so please offer input when you have something to contribute. In order to get through all the materials, I may suggest a time limit for discussions.

When it comes to the writing exercises, please don't worry if you don't get as much writing done during the Workshop Session as you'd like; you can continue to work on this at home. You are encouraged to write something each time because often that effort leads to the words you were hoping for. It's more important that you at least start each exercise so that we can share our ideas and learn from the feedback of others.

After we write, we will "workshop" our writing. I'll ask for volunteers to read their writing exercises. The most useful feedback is positive, specific and constructive.

Let's get started!"

For the facilitator

Leading the "workshopping" segment is more about common sense than expertise. So, follow these simple guidelines and let the workshop members take it from there.

The goals of this Ethical Will workshop are to:

- *Acknowledge your beliefs and values, life lessons and hopes for the future.*
- *Create an Ethical Will that reveals the essence of what you stand for and how you want to be remembered.*
- *Set a tone and include examples and details that reinforce your message as well as give your loved ones a sense of your ethical spirit.*

Remember that the role of the workshop attendees is much the same as that of the loved ones who will share these Ethical Wills; it is invaluable to the creator of each Ethical Will to know whether the message being sent is the message being received. As is true in most of life, the best rule for workshop etiquette is *The Golden Rule.*

1. Ask for a volunteer to read his or her writing exercise. *(Be prepared to start by reading yours if no volunteer is forthcoming.)*

2. Limit the reading to one double-spaced page or 300 words *(just in case an attendee totes along the Ethical Treatise he or she has been toiling over for years).*

3. Remind attendees that feedback should reflect the goals of *acknowledging, recording and effectively sharing your ethical legacy.* Focus on the clarity of the message and its *ethical* essence, not its grammatical or literary essence.

4. Comments/feedback should always be:

- **Positive**
  Feedback don't: *"That first paragraph really rambled."*
  Feedback do: *"It might be more effective for your loved ones if you have one sentence at the beginning, the key [value, lesson or hope] you are sharing and then expand on it. Key messages help to focus us both as writers and as listeners."*
- **Specific**
  Feedback don't: *"I don't know—it's just confusing to me."*

Feedback do: *"I don't quite understood what you meant in that first sentence. Can you tell us more about the message you want to convey?"*

- **Helpful/constructive**

Feedback don't: *"There's no depth or details."*

Feedback do: *"What you've said so far makes me want to hear more. Can you include some examples of how you came to hold these beliefs?"*

To be honest, a workshop that includes all the discussion questions and writing exercises contained in *The Workshop Edition of SO GROWS THE TREE* is an ambitious undertaking, so don't hesitate to pick and choose which ones of either category sound most interesting to the most people. And you may find that you want to extend your time together for discussion groups and a cup of coffee or supplementary writing and workshopping sessions. That's one of the advantages of *The Workshop Edition of SO GROWS THE TREE*: it's all yours—do what works for you and your group members.

So, there you have it—and it doesn't sound nearly as difficult or intimidating as you thought it would, does it? Jot down the names of a few people right now who you think would be interested and then ask each one to provide two more names to you. You've got the beginning of a workshop group!

And, if you think of it, drop me an e-mail to let me know about your experience. I'm eager to improve The Workshop Edition of SO GROWS THE TREE *in any way I can and make it as user- and writer-friendly as possible (visit www.SoGrowsTheTree.com for contact information).* **Learn from the past, live for today and hope for the future.**

᠙ Notes to Self ᠙

Somewhere, something incredible is waiting to be known.
Dr. Carl Sagan

ஃ Endnotes and References ☙

[1] Term used to describe American Army infantrymen through the end of World War I, www.worldwar1.com.
[2] James Harold Godfred "Bill" Kline, June 21, 1901–July 31, 1977.

[3] Marian Isabel (McCollum) Kline, September 12, 1904–December 28, 1977.

[4] Letter from J. H. "Bill" Kline to Eugene Lawrence "Dutch" Kline reprinted in its entirety except for omitted personal references.
[5] Eugene Lawrence "Dutch" Kline, October 18, 1910 – September 22, 1982.

[6] United Airlines Flight 297, crashed on November 23, 1962 en route from Newark, New Jersey to Washington, D.C. after striking a flock of whistling swans, killing all aboard. www.aviation-safety.net. Mary Kathryn Kline, June 11, 1940–November 23, 1962.

[7] Genesis 49, *The Holy Bible, Revised Standard Version* (New York: Thomas Nelson & Sons, 1953).

[8] Israel Abrahams, *Chapters on Jewish Literature* (The Jewish Publication Society of America, 1899), Chapter XIX. Ethical Literature, www.Gutenberg.org.

[9] Ibid.

[10] Ibid.

[11] *The Norton Anthology of American Literature* (New York: W. W. Norton & Company, Inc., 1999) pp. 127-128 and 144-147.

[12] "Historical Document: Sullivan Ballou Letter," The Civil War: A Film by Ken Burns, Public Broadcasting Service, www.pbs.org/civilwar/war/ballou_letter.html.

[13] Jack Riemer and Nathaniel Stampfer, *So That Your Values Live On—Ethical Wills and How to Prepare Them* (Woodstock, Vermont: Jewish Lights Publishing, 1991) pp. 41-56. To purchase, visit www.JewishLights.com. This book is a bounty of Ethical Will examples from the ages. For an archive of farewell letters (Ethical Wills) from the Holocaust, visit www.yadvashem.org.

[14] This is a good time to cover the topic of documents that, although relevant to a discussion of mortality and/or immortality, should not be confused with Ethical Wills.

- **Power of Attorney**: A written authorization for an agent to transact business on behalf of another, the principal.
- **Durable Power of Attorney for Financial Matters**: A power of attorney that authorizes the agent to act on behalf of the principal, once the principal loses the capacity to act on her or his own behalf.
- **Durable Power of Attorney for Health Care**: A document in which a person delegates to another (the proxy) the authority to make medical and health care decisions.
- **Living Will:** A document that specifies the patient's wishes for end-of-life care in the event of a terminal or irreversible condition.
- **Living Trust:** An entity created for the purpose of holding assets while the grantor retains the use and enjoyment of the property (often used to title one's home).
- **Last Will and Testament:** An instrument that provides for the disposition of a person's real and personal property upon death and for the custody and care of dependents.
- **Letter of Instructions:** A document supplementing one's Last Will and Testament that contains information on the location of important documents, persons to be notified at time of death and burial and memorial directions.

Each one of these is a legal document. An Ethical Will is not a legal document. Except for a Letter of Instructions, each of these documents requires a notarized signature and perhaps witnesses as well. An Ethical Will does not. Any one of these could end up being read by strangers (e.g., in a hospital file or in the public probate records). An Ethical Will won't, unless you decide to share it with those beyond your circle of loved ones. Jacob's oral Ethical Will included his final wishes for burial. Although I recommend making one's own funeral and burial arrangements and providing a detailed Letter of Instructions, the modern Ethical Will is not usually the place for that information.

Each of these documents is a valuable part of taking responsibility for one's self, planning for circumstances that are not just possible, they are inevitable. As you prepare to create your Ethical Will, also please check this list of legal documentation and make arrangements to obtain any you need. And once you do, discuss them with your loved ones. For further information, see: *Last things first, just in case... The practical guide to Living Wills and Durable Powers of Attorney for Health Care* by Jo Kline Cebuhar, J.D. (West Des Moines, Iowa: Murphy Publishing, 2006). To purchase, visit www.MurphyPublishing.com or www.Amazon.com.

[15] Iris Murdoch, *The Sea, The Sea* (New York: The Penguin Group, 1978) p. 2. To purchase, visit www.Penguin.com.

[16] Patrick Lennox, "Alexander Pope" in The Catholic Encyclopedia (New York: Robert Appleton Company, 1911), www.newadvent.org. Interview with Robert Speed, September 30, 2009, who is a literary scholar and retired professor of literature, Grand View University, Des Moines, Iowa. Alexander Pope: May 22, 1688 – May 30, 1744.

[17] U.S. Department of Commerce, Bureau of the Census, "Projections of the Number of Households and Families in the United States: 1995 to 2010," 1996, www.census.gov, p. 6.

[18] "Butterfly effect," www.en.wikipedia.org/wiki/Butterfly_effect.

[19] The Allianz American Legacies Study, conducted in 2005 by The Allianz Life Insurance Company of North America in collaboration with Dr. Ken Dychtwald of Age Wave, www.allianzlife.com.

[20] Jo Kline Cebuhar, www.SoGrowsTheTree.com.

[21] See Note 14 above for a brief discussion of life-planning legal documents.

[22] Kay Lyons, former librarian and author of children's books. www.PeriplusPublishingGroup.com.

[23] Joan Halifax, *Being with Dying – Cultivating Compassion and Fearlessness in the Presence of Death* (Boston: Shambhala Publications, 2008) p. 11. To purchase, visit www.upaya.org.

[24] Genesis 49, *The Holy Bible, Revised Standard Version* (New York: Thomas Nelson & Sons, 1953).

[25] Edward M. Kennedy, "Tribute to Senator Robert F. Kennedy," (November 20, 1925-June 6, 1968) delivered at St. Patrick's Cathedral, New York City, New York, on June 8, 1968, www.jfklibrary.org.

[26] Jo Kline Cebuhar, "Eulogy for Wesley J. Kline," November 22, 1955–November 22, 1998.

[27] Jo Kline Cebuhar, "Eulogy for Anthony Cebuhar, November 23, 1906-March 25, 1999.

[28] Sharon Christa Corrigan McAuliffe, September 2, 1948–January 28, 1986. Visit www.christa.org for information about the ongoing programs at the Christa McAuliffe Center, Framingham State College, in Framingham, Massachusetts.

[29] Peggy Noonan, *On Speaking Well* (New York: HarperCollins Publishers, 1998) p. 162. (Hardover originally published as *Simply Speaking* in 1998.) Visit www.PeggyNoonan.com to learn more about Peggy and to purchase her books.

[30] Ibid., p. 162.

[31] Ibid., p. 164.

[32] *Merriam-Webster's Collegiate Dictionary*, 10th Edition, 1996, p. 400.

[33] Tim Russert, *Big Russ & Me* (New York: Miramax Books, 2005) p. 576. To purchase, visit www.HyperionBooks.com.

[34] Herbert Marshall McLuhan, July 21, 1911 - December 31, 1980.

[35] Riemer and Stampfer, p. 170.

[36] Ibid.

[37] Carnegie Mellon University Lectures Series "Journeys," www.cmu.edu/uls.

[38] Randy Pausch with Jeffrey Zaslow, *The Last Lecture* (New York: Hyperion, 2008) p. 3. To view Randy Pausch's last lecture at Carnegie Mellon and to purchase the DVD or book, visit www.TheLastLecture.com.

[39] Ibid., p. 9.

[40] Ibid.

[41] Randy Pausch, "Really Achieving Your Childhood Dreams," DVD (Philadelphia, Pennsylvania: Carnegie Mellon University, 2007). Available for viewing at www.YouTube.com and at www.TheLastLecture.com.

[42] Randy Pausch and Jeffrey Zaslow, page 8.

[43] Tim Russert, *Wisdom of Our Fathers* (New York: Random House, 2006) pp. 51-52. To purchase, visit www.RandomHouse.com.

[44] For an advance directive form that combines the instructions of a Living Will with the appointment of a Durable Power of Attorney for Health Care, visit www.agingwithdignity.org to obtain *Five Wishes*, an advance directive form accepted in 42 states (check the list to see if it is accepted in your state). It is a user-friendly booklet that walks you—and your loved ones—through the decision-making and documentation process.

[45] Encarta® World English Dictionary (North American Edition) 2009, Microsoft Corporation, www.encarta.msn.com.

[46] From the eulogy for Chuckles the Clown, "Chuckles Bites the Dust," Mary Tyler More Show, CBS, 1970-1977, www.wikipedia.org.

[47] Tim Russert, *Big Russ & Me,* p. 576.

[48] Jon Huntsman, *Winners Never Cheat – Even in Difficult Times* (Upper Saddle River, New Jersey: Wharton School Publishing, 2009) p. 205.

[49] Louis S. Schafer, *Tombstones of Your Ancestors* (Westminster, Maryland: Heritage Books, Inc., 2007) pp. 21-22.

[50] Candelaria, Nash, "John Wayne, Person and Persona: The love affairs of an American legend," Hopscotch: A Cultural Review - Volume 2, Number 4, 2001, pp. 2–13, Duke University Press.

[51] www.quotationspage.com
www.bartleby.com
www.quoteland.com
www.thinkexist.com
www.theotherpages.org/quote.html
www.quotegarden.com
www.brainyquote.com

[52] Quotations:

Always be nice to children—
they are the ones who will choose your rest home.
- Phyllis Diller

It's never too late to be what you might have been.
- George Elliott

[53] Mary Kay Shanley, www.MaryKayShanley.com. Quotations:
Either you are interesting
At any age or you are not.
- Katherine Hepburn

Safe, for a child, is her father's hand, holding her tight.
- Marion C. Garretty

[54] "Mark Twain," America's Story from America's Library, Library of Congress, www.americaslibrary.gov.

[55] Attributed to Ralph Waldo Emerson although there is a dispute about its origin. Some credit Bessie (Mrs. A. J.) Stanley of Lincoln County, Kansas, who wrote an exceptionally similar essay for a contest in the Lincoln Sentinel, published on November 30, 1905. "Success," www.transcendentalists.com.

[56] Randy Pausch with Jeffrey Zaslow, *The Last Lecture* (New York: Hyperion, 2008). To purchase, visit www.TheLastLecture.com.

[57] Anne Morrow Lindbergh, *Gift from the Sea* (New York: Pantheon Books, 2005 reprint of 1955 book). To purchase, visit www.RandomHouse.com.

[58] Tim Russert, *Big Russ & Me* (New York: Miramax Books, 2005) p. 576. To purchase, visit www.HyperionBooks.com.

[59] Tim Russert, *Wisdom of Our Fathers* (New York: Random House, 2006). To purchase, visit www.RandomHouse.com.

[60] Mitch Albom, *Tuesdays with Morrie* (New York: Doubleday, 1997). To purchase, visit www.RandomHouse.com or www.TuesdaysWithMorrie.com.

[61] Elisabeth Kubler-Ross and David Kessler, *Life Lessons* (New York: Scribner, 2000). To purchase, visit www.EKRFoundation.org.

[62] God, et al., *The Holy Bible, Revised Standard Version* (New York: Thomas Nelson & Sons, 1953).

[63] Gwen Cooper, *Homer's Odyssey* (New York: Delacorte Press, 2009). To purchase, visit www.GwenCooper.com.

[64] Mark Twain, *Life on the Mississippi* (Boston: James R. Osgood and Company, 1883). To download a free e-book, visit www.Gutenberg.org.

[65] Bill Bryson, *The Life and Times of the Thunderbolt Kid* (New York: Broadway Books, 2006). To purchase, visit www.RandomHouse.com.

[66] Jay Allison and Dan Gediman, Editors, *This I Believe, The Personal Philosophies of Remarkable Men and Women* (New York: Henry Holt and Company, 2006). To purchase, visit www.ThisIBelieve.org.

[67] Mitch Albom, *have a little faith, a true story* (New York: Hyperion Books, 2009). To purchase, visit www.MitchAlbom.com.

[68] Jim Stovall, *The Ultimate Gift* (Colorado Springs, Colorado: David C. Cook, 2007). To purchase, visit www.TheUltimateGift.com.

[69] Jon Huntsman, *Winners Never Cheat – Even in Difficult Times* (Upper Saddle River, New Jersey: Wharton School Publishing, 2009). To purchase, visit www.FTPress.com.

[70] Roger Rosenblatt, *making toast* (New York: Harper Collins, 2010). To purchase, visit www.HarperCollins.com.

[71] Judith Lodden, "What I learned from my Mom," lodden@SportsMinded.com.

[72] May (Murphy) Nelson, "The Thing I Value Most" (1886 – 1931).

[73] C. W. Kline and FatCat Fort, Bruno and Ernie Cebuhar and Wyatt and Ellie Kline.

[74] Stan Rawlinson, "The 10 Commandments From a Pet's Standpoint," www.doglistener.co.uk.

[75] Online Etymology Dictionary, www.etymonline.com.

[76] Anthony Cebuhar (November 23, 1906-March 25, 1999):

For today and its blessings,
I owe the world an attitude of gratitude.
- Clarence E. Hodges

Wesley J. Kline (November 22, 1955-November 22, 1998):

We can't all be heroes because
someone has to sit on the curb and clap as they go by.
- Will Rogers

Roy Z. Fort (October 6, 1949-September 5, 1979):

To love is to receive a glimpse of heaven.
- Karen Sunde

[77] Hannah (Smith) Kline, January 19, 1874 - May 2, 1932. Quotation:

A man finds room in a few square inches of his face
for the traits of all his ancestors;
for the expression of all his history, and his wants.
– Ralph Waldo Emerson

78 Elizabeth (Hardie) Jones, 1882 - 1974. Poems:

Two frogs fell into a deep cream bowl,
One was an optimistic soul;
But the other took the gloomy view,
"We shall drown," he cried, without more ado.
So with a last despairing cry,
He flung up his legs and he said "Goodbye."
Quoth the other frog with a merry grin,
"I can't get out, but I won't give in.
I'll just swim around till my strength is spent,
Then will I die the more content."

Bravely he swam till it would seem
His struggles began to churn the cream.
On the top of the butter at last he stopped,
And out of the bowl he gayly hopped.
What of the moral? 'Tis easily found:
IF YOU CAN'T HOP OUT, KEEP SWIMMING 'ROUND.

[I believe this is attributable to Walter B. Knight, from his 1956 book *Knight's Master Book of 4000 Illustrations*, popularly "borrowed" for use in countless church sermons.]

The man who once most wisely said,
"Be sure you're right, then go ahead,"
Might well have added this, to wit:
"Be sure you're wrong before you quit."

[Found, without attribution, in *The Rotarian, The Magazine of Service*, August 1920; no doubt lifted from that magazine and used in yet another church sermon...]
79"Scrapbooking," www.en.wikipedia.org.
80 Ibid.
81"History of Scrapbooking," www.everything-about-scrapbooking.com.
82 Edward Wakeling, "The Lewis Carroll Scrapbook Collection: The Lewis Carroll Scrapbook," http://international.loc.gov/intldl/carrollhtml/lcwakeling.html.
83"Mark Twain's Interactive Scrapbook," www.pbs.org/marktwain/scrapbook/index.html.
84 Roy Z. Fort, Faith Ann Fort, Helen Fort, Walter Fort. The poem:
Do not stand at my grave and weep;
I am not there. I do not sleep.
I am a thousand winds that blow.
I am the diamond glints on snow.
I am the sunlight on ripened grain.
I am the gentle autumn rain.

When you awaken in the morning's hush
I am the swift uplifting rush
Of quiet birds in circled flight.
I am the soft stars that shine at night.
Do not stand at my grave and cry;
I am not there. I did not die.
- Mary Elizabeth Frye

[85] Eugene L. Kline (October 18, 1910-September 22, 1982) and Catherine Elizabeth (Jones) Kline (October 27, 1916-January 30, 2010). Quotation:

Marriage is our last, best chance to grow up.
- Joseph Barth

[86] Marian Isabel (McCullom) Kline's Chicken Divan (this is the original version; for an updated touch, try using artichoke hearts, sliced water chestnuts or spinach instead of broccoli and substitute Italian Five Cheeses for the American cheese. As with most really great comfort foods, this is guaranteed *not* to be low-calorie):

```
                        Chicken Divan
2 - 10 oz. pkgs frozen      2 cans cream chicken soup
       Broccoli             1 c. mayonnaise or salad dressing
2 c. sliced cooked          1 t. lemon juice
       Chicken or 3 chicken ½ t. curry powder
       breasts, cooked and  ½ c. shredded sharp process
       boned                       American cheese
                        ********
½ c. soft bread crumbs    1 T. butter
Cook broccoli in boiling salted water till tender;
Drain.  Arrange broccoli in greased 11 x 7 pan.  Place chicken on
top.  Combine soup, mayonnaise, lemon juice, and curry powder; pour
over chicken. Sprinkle with cheese.  Combine bread crumbs and
butter; sprinkle over all.  Bake in 350o oven — 25 to 30 mins.
6 to 8 servings.
```

Marian "Isabel" (McCollum) Kline
(September 12, 1904 – December 28, 1977)
Gracious, dignified, organized, compassionate,
nurturing, gifted cook, hostess and homemaker.
Wife of Uncle Bill Kline,
Mother of cousin Mary Kathryn.

[87] Scrapbooking," www.en.wikipedia.org.

[88] The easiest way to start is to Google "free clip art."   From those 20,000,000 results you can glean the sites that are truly free (no royalty fee, no subscription fee) for download.

Microsoft also has an extensive free clip art site accessible within its software or you can visit at www.office.microsoft.com/en-us/images/.

[89] Randy Pausch, "Really Achieving Your Childhood Dreams," DVD (Philadelphia, Pennsylvania: Carnegie Mellon University, 2007). Video accessible at www.cmu.edu/randyslecture.

[90] "Lessons of a Lifetime," Hebrew Home of Greater Washington, D.C., www.hebrew-home.org.

[91] The easiest way to start is to Google "free recording software." From those 13,800,000 results you can glean the sites that are truly free for download. Or go directly to www.Audacity.sourceforge.net.

[92] *Turn Turn Turn:* Lyrics – Book of Ecclesiastes; music – Pete Seger.

[93] *Deep Peace:* Lyrics – Gaelic blessing; music – Bill Douglas.

[94] *Now and Forever:* Lyrics and music by Carole King.

[95] *Sunny Side of the Street:* Lyrics – Dorothy Fields; music – Jimmy McHugh.

[96] *Dream a Little Dream of Me:* Lyrics – Gus Kahn; music – Fabian Andre and Wilbur Schwandt.

[97] *The Four Seasons, Opus 8 No. 1:* Antonio Vivaldi.

[98] *Adagio for Strings, Opus 11:* Samuel Barber.

[99] *We're in the Club Now* (from Pixar's movie *Up*): Michael Giacchino.

[100] *As Time Goes By:* Lyrics and music by Herman Hupfeld.

[101] *Somewhere Over the Rainbow:* Lyrics - E. Y. Harburg; music - Harold Arlen.

[102] *When You Wish Upon a Star:* Lyrics and music by Ned Washington and Leigh Harline.

[103] *It Is Well With My Soul:* Lyrics by Horatio Spafford; music by Philip Bliss. Spafford penned these words while sailing to England after his four daughters were lost at sea in the wreck of the ship *Ville Du Havre* on November 22, 1873.

[104] *Spirit in the Sky:* Lyrics and music by Norman Greenbaum.

[105] *Circle of Life* (featured in Disney's 1994 movie *The Lion King*): Lyrics – Tim Rice; music – Elton John.

[106] "Memory Jugs," The Ames Gallery, www.amesgallery.com.

[107] Peggy Noonan, p. 162.

[108] *The Times of Your Life:* Lyrics – Bill Lane; music – Roger Nichols [authorship often mistakenly attributed to Paul Anka, who sang the song for the Kodak commercial and the #1 Billboard.]

[109] Try www.BillBoard.com, www.Amazon.com or www.BN.com for historical record charts and tunes to sample or to download.

[110] Franklin Junior High School, Des Moines, Iowa, Mr. Charles Newton's 7th Grade homeroom class, 1963.

[111] The Rick and Ann (Love) Pauley family of Clive, Iowa (Jake, Max, Ben, Katie and Houston). Quotation:

While we try to teach our children all about life,
Our children teach us what life is all about.
– Angela Schwindt

[112] To read an inspiring assortment of Ethical Eulogies and Ethical Tributes delivered to honor Rabbi Richard J. Israel (1929-2000), www.site38.com/dickisrael/default.htm.
[113] Max Ehrmann, *The Poems of Max Ehrmann* (New York: Dodge Publishing Company, 1910), pp. 178-179.
[114] "Desiderata" by Max Ehrmann. Copyright 1927 by Max Ehrmann. Public Domain 1976 by judgment of the United States 7th Circuit Court of Appeals.

Desiderata
by Max Ehrmann

Go placidly amid the noise and haste,
and remember what peace there may be in silence.
As far as possible without surrender
be on good terms with all persons.

Speak your truth quietly and clearly;
and listen to others, even the dull and the ignorant;
they too have their story.

Avoid loud and aggressive persons,
they are vexations to the spirit.
If you compare yourself with others,
you may become vain and bitter;
for always there will be greater
and lesser persons than yourself.

Enjoy your achievements as well as your plans.
Keep interested in your own career, however humble;
it is a real possession in the changing fortunes of time.
Exercise caution in your business affairs;
for the world is full of trickery.
But let this not blind you to what virtue there is;
many persons strive for high ideals;
and everywhere life is full of heroism.

Be yourself.
Especially, do not feign affection.
Neither be cynical about love;
for in the face of all aridity and disenchantment
it is as perennial as the grass.

Take kindly the counsel of the years,
gracefully surrendering the things of youth.
Nurture strength of spirit to shield you in sudden misfortune.
But do not distress yourself with dark imaginings.

Many fears are born of fatigue and loneliness.
Beyond a wholesome discipline, be gentle with yourself.

You are a child of the universe,
no less than the trees and the stars;
you have a right to be here.
And whether or not it is clear to you,
no doubt the universe is unfolding as it should.

Therefore be at peace with God,
whatever you conceive Him to be,
and whatever your labors and aspirations,
in the noisy confusion of life keep peace with your soul.

With all its sham, drudgery, and broken dreams,
it is still a beautiful world.
Be cheerful. Strive to be happy.

[115] *Robert L. Bell dba Crescendo Publishing Company vs. Combined Registry Company,* United States Court of Appeals, 536 F.2d 164 (7th Cir., 1976).

[116] "Desiderata," Old St. Paul's Episcopal Church, Baltimore, www.temp.osp1692.org.

[117] "Desiderata," www.wikipedia.org/wiki/Desiderata.

[118] "Les Crane," www.en.wikipedia.org/wiki/Les_Crane.

[119] "Info about Desiderta," attributed to Sam McGarrity at Guideposts magazine, www.vbraren.de/desi_inf.htm.

[120] *Robert L. Bell dba Crescendo Publishing Company vs. Combined Registry Company.*

[121] "Star-Spangled Banner and the War of 1812," Encyclopedia Smithsonian, www.si.edu.

[122] NEDCC (Northeast Document Conservation Center), "Resources for private and Family Collections," www.nedcc.org/resources/family.php.

[123] "Mounting Collections in Albums and Scrapbooks," U.S. National Archives and Records Administration, www.archives.gov/preservation/family-archives.

[124] "A guide to preserving scanned documents and images," CompUSA, www.static.compusa.com [no longer accessible May 1, 2011].

[125] Lincoln Spector, "Answer Line: Will my CD-R and DVD+R Discs Still Run in 10 Years?", PC World Magazine website, www.pcworld.com.

[126] Fred R. Byers, "Care and Handling of CDs and DVDs: A Guide for Librarians and Archivists," published by Council on Library and Information Resources and National Institute of Standards and Technology, www.clir.org.

[127] "Caring for your photographic collections," The Library of Congress, Preservation, www.loc.gov.

[128] Ibid. Also visit The Northeast Document Conservation Center website for info on preserving family collections (www.nedcc.org/resources/family.php) and The U.S. Nat'l Archives and Records Administration (www.archives.gov).

129 U.S. Nat'l Archives and Records Administration, "Records Emergency Information," www.archives.gov.

130 See The American Institute for Conservation of Historic and Artistic Works (AIC) website for detailed information on storage and preservation of family heirlooms as well as a directory of professional conservators and archivists: www.conservation-us.org. www.familyarchives.com is just one of many sites dedicated to methods and supplies for preserving family historical documents.

*Life is no brief candle to me; it is a sort of splendid torch which
I've got a hold of for the moment and I want to make it burn
as brightly as possible before handing it on to future generations.*
George Bernard Shaw

℅ Notes to Self ℀

If a composer could say what he had to say in words
he would not bother trying to say it in music.
Gustav Mahler

❧ References for the narrated slideshow ☙

In addition to the citations contained in this book's *Endnotes and References*, credit is due for images and songs that appear in the DVD that accompanies this book.

Most clipart images are from *www.office.microsoft.com/en-us/images/*. If not, they were scanned images from the author's collection of stuff.

Images of persons other than really famous people are from the author's library of photographs. All others are provided as research and/or examples by the author, in keeping with the author's desire to introduce and credit those who have produced outstanding examples of ethical writing throughout history. The author encourages the reader to obtain copies of these works and read them in their entirety. Although the *Endnotes and References* direct the reader to each publisher's site for purchase, if available, most books (even those now out-of-print) can also be found through your local bookseller or on sites such as *www.Amazon.com*, *www.BarnesandNoble.com* and *www.BooksAMillion.com* or at your local library.

As for the music that is part of this narrated slideshow, the author used excerpts from the sound recordings credited below. The reader is encouraged to patronize sites such as *www.itunes.com*, *www.Amazon.com*, *www.BN.com*, *www.NaxosMusicLibrary.com* and *www.Rhapsody.com* to purchase individual tracks or entire albums for personal use. The reader will also find that many traditional on-line retailers now provide music libraries for purchase and download.

Piano music throughout the narrated slideshow
Title: **Bethena – A Concert Waltz**
Composer: Scott Joplin
Copyright: public domain
Performer: Tom Pascale

The reader is encouraged to visit *www.PianoSociety.com* for a library of exceptional musical performances by a variety of artists from around the world, available for download without charge, strictly for personal use. *The Piano Society* (based in Sweden) is a nonprofit internet site wholly funded by charitable contributions, and the reader is encouraged to support its work.

To Tom Pascale of New York, a special thank you for treasuring his mother's insistence
on piano lessons for each of her six children and for so generously allowing
the author to include his recording of Bethena *as part of this narrated slideshow.*

6-11 Shown in this slide is the advance directive form, *Five Wishes*. It combines the instructions of a Living Will with the appointment of a Durable Power of Attorney for Health Care and is accepted in 42 states (check the list at *www.AgingWithDignity.org* to verify whether your state is included). It is a user-friendly booklet/legal document that walks you—and your loved ones—through the process of preparing effective end-of-life health care directives. Visit the non-profit site *www.AgingWithDignity.org* to order copies for you and your loved ones to discuss and complete.

10-30
Title: **Turn Turn Turn**
Composer: Music by Pete Seger; Lyrics from the Bible's *Book of Ecclesiastes*
Recording copyright: CBS Records
Performer: The Byrds

10-31
Title: **Deep Peace**
Composer: Music by Bill Douglas; Lyrics from a Gaelic blessing
Recording copyright: Singing Heart Productions
Performer: Shaina Noll

10-32
Title: **Now and Forever**
Composer: Carole King
Recording copyright: Lushmole Music
Performer: Carole King

10-33
Title: **On the Sunny Side of the Street**
Composer: Music by Jimmy McHugh; Lyrics by Dorothy Fields
Recording copyright: Aldi Music
Performer: The Manhattan Transfer

10-34
Title: **Dream a Little Dream of Me**
Composer: Music by Fabian Andre and Wilbur Schwandt; Lyrics by Gus Kahn
Recording copyright: MCA Records, Inc.
Performer: The Mamas and The Papas

10-36
Title: **The Four Seasons, Opus 8 No. 1**
Composer: Antonio Vivaldi
Recording copyright: HNH International Ltd.
Performer: Failoni Chamber Orchestra of Budapest

10-37
Title: **Adagio for Strings, Opus 11**
Composer: Samuel Barber
Recording copyright: HNH International Ltd.
Performer: Cappella Istropolitana Chamber Orchestra

10-38
Title: **We're In the Club Now** (Soundtrack to Disney/Pixar's movie *Up*)
Composer: Michael Giacchino
Recording copyright: Disney Enterprises, Inc./Pixar
Performer: Music Orchestrated and Conducted by Tim Simonec

10-39
Title: **An Affair to Remember**
Composer: Music by Harry Warren; Lyrics by Leo McCarey and Harold Adamson
Recording copyright: 20th Century Fox Film Corporation/Sony Music Entertainment
Performer: The 20th Century Fox Orchestra and Chorus

10-40
Title: **As Time Goes By**
Composer: Music and lyrics by Herman Hupfeld
Recording copyright: Turner Entertainment Co.
Performer: Dooley Wilson (vocal) and Elliot Carpenter (piano)

10-41
Title: **Somewhere Over the Rainbow**
Composer: Music by Harold Arlen; Lyrics by E. Y. Harburg
Recording copyright: Turner Entertainment Co.
Performer: Judy Garland

10-43
Title: **When You Wish Upon a Star**
Composer: Music and lyrics by Leigh Harline and Ned Washington
Recording copyright: Buena Vista Pictures Distribution, Inc.
Performer: Cliff Edwards

10-45
Title: **When You Wish Upon a Star**
Composer: Music and lyrics by Leigh Harline and Ned Washington
Recording copyright: Sony Music Entertainment Inc.
Performer: The Mormon Tabernacle Choir

10-46
Title: **It Is Well With My Soul**
Composer: Music by Philip Bliss; Lyrics by Horatio Spafford
Spafford penned these words while sailing to England after his four daughters (eleven-year-old Anna "Annie", nine-year-old Margaret Lee, five-year-old Elizabeth "Bessie", and two-year-old Tanetta) were lost at sea in the wreck of the ship Ville Du Havre on November 22, 1873.
Recording copyright: INO Records, LLC
Performer: Sandi Patty

10-47
Title: **Spirit In the Sky**
Composer: Music and lyrics by Norman Greenbaum
Recording copyright: Westminster Music Ltd.
Performer: Norman Greenbaum

10-48
Title: **Circle of Life** (Soundtrack to Disney's movie *Lion King*)
Composer: Music by Elton John; Lyrics by Tim Rice
Recording copyright: Sony Music Entertainment Inc.
Performer: The Mormon Tabernacle Choir

JOHN KLINE'S FUNERAL RITES HELD MARCH 25

Late North Western Railroad Employe Was Native of Germany, Coming to U. S. When 11.

Final respects were paid to the memory of the late John Kline at funeral rites he~~~ noon ~~~

In 1892 he was united in marriage with Hannah Smith of Moingona. To this union were born five children. Clarence died in infancy. Frank Kline resides at Paton, Iowa, J. H. Kline in Clinton, Iowa, Mrs. L. D. Sturtz at Boone, and Gene Kline at Boone. Mrs. Hannah Kline passed away on May 2, 1932.

Was a Mason.

Mr. Kline spent his entire life as an employee of the railroad company with the exception of the period 1909 to 1921 when he engaged in farming. On January 16, 1935, he was united in marriage to Alma Exzell of Boone, who remains to mourn his passing. He passed away on March 22, 1938, at the age of 69 years, 5 months and 2 days. In addition to the children and widow there are 10 grandchildren who remain.

He was a member of Mount Olive Lodge No. 79, A. F. & A. M. of Boone and DeMolay Consistory of Clinton, Iowa. He was also a member and past Noble Grand of the Independent Order of Odd Fellows and a member of the Rebeccas. Mr. Kline was one of the early members of the Kum-Bak class of the Christian church of Boone and regularly attended this class for the past 12 years.

He supported the simple philosophy in life that people should put forth their best efforts without thought of reward or personal gain. His recreations and wants in life were simple and few but he gave everything—a philanthrophy that could not be greater.

As published March 28, 1938, in the *Boone* [Iowa] *News-Republican*,
the obituary for the author's paternal grandfather,

John Kline
October 20, 1868 – March 22, 1938

(discovered and first viewed by the author on May 1, 2011)

People grow through experience
if they meet life honestly and courageously.
This is how character is built.
Eleanor Roosevelt

෨ **Notes to Self** ෬